THE TREATMENT AND PREVENTION
OF READING PROBLEMS

(Eighth Printing)

The Treatment And Prevention Of Reading Problems

(THE NEURO-PSYCHOLOGICAL APPROACH)

By

CARL H. DELACATO, Ed.D.

*Head of the Junior and Middle Schools, Chestnut Hill Academy,
Philadelphia, Pennsylvania*

*Director of Psychological Services, The Rehabilitation Center at
Philadelphia, Philadelphia, Pennsylvania*

*Affiliated Instructor in Rehabilitation Nursing,
Lankenau Hospital School of Nursing,
Philadelphia, Pennsylvania*

*Director of The Reading Clinic, Chestnut Hill Academy,
Philadelphia, Pennsylvania*

CHARLES C THOMAS · PUBLISHER

Springfield · Illinois · U.S.A.

Published and Distributed Throughout the World by
CHARLES C THOMAS • PUBLISHER
BANNERSTONE HOUSE
301-327 East Lawrence Avenue, Springfield, Illinois, U.S.A.
NATCHEZ PLANTATION HOUSE
735 North Atlantic Boulevard, Fort Lauderdale, Florida, U.S.A.

© 1959 *by* CHARLES C THOMAS • PUBLISHER

Library of Congress Catalog Card Number: 59-6742

First Printing, 1959, 2500 copies
Second Printing, 1961, 2500 copies
Third Printing, 1963, 2000 copies
Fourth Printing, 1965, 2000 copies
Fifth Printing, 1966, 2000 copies
Sixth Printing, 1966, 2000 copies
Seventh Printing, 1968, 2000 copies
Eighth Printing, 1971, 2000 copies

With THOMAS BOOKS careful attention is given to all details of manufacturing and design. It is the Publisher's desire to present books that are satisfactory as to their physical qualities and artistic possibilities and appropriate for their particular use. THOMAS BOOKS will be true to those laws of quality that assure a good name and good will.

Printed in the United States of America
J-1

To Janice, my wife

PREFACE

Through verbal communication, children are assimilated into the culture. In the past, children who could not hear or speak were looked upon with awe. Their acceptance into the social framework was tenuous because the members of their group could not communicate with them. This lack of the ability to communicate led many times to the rejection and exploitation of these children by their culture.

As an extension of the above, today's children who are unable to read or who do not read well receive a great deal of attention from both the general public and educators. This attention on the part of the general public tends to be critical of education. The public usually blames instances of poor reading on the system of reading used, the lack of phonetic instruction, poor school discipline or just poor teaching.

Educators, aware of this criticism, have tried many avenues for the elimination of the non-reading or poor-reading handicap. There remain, however, a number of children who do not read up to the level indicated by their capacity. It is these children, their teachers and parents, to whom this work is directed.

ACKNOWLEDGMENTS

THE author wishes to acknowledge his indebtedness to the staff of Chestnut Hill Academy and to the staff of The Rehabilitation Center at Philadelphia for their constant help and encouragement.

He wishes to acknowledge his great indebtedness to Mr. Robert A. Kingsley, Headmaster of Chestnut Hill Academy for his constant guidance and encouragement.

He is indebted to Dr. Ralph Preston, Director of the Reading Clinic, University of Pennsylvania, who introduced him to the fascinating problem of remedial reading.

He is also indebted to Mr. Morton MacTurk, Director of The Chestnut Hill Rehabilitation Center, Philadelphia, and to Dr. Martin Palmer, Director, Institute of Logopedics, Wichita, Kansas, and to one of his co-workers at the Institute, Mr. Claude Cheek.

The author wishes to acknowledge his indebtedness to Temple Fay, M.D., F.A.C.S., the dean of modern neurosurgery, who during the years of 1953-1956 through his teaching and guidance stimulated the author toward initiating this study. The author wishes to acknowledge his great indebtedness to Robert J. Doman, M.D., Medical Director of The Rehabilitation Center at Philadelphia.

The author wishes to acknowledge his greatest indebtedness to Glenn J. Doman, Director of The Rehabilitation Center at Philadelphia for his constant encouragement, teaching and guidance during the past six years. The author is also indebted to Lindley Boyer, Mary

Blackburn, Mary Jane Swain, and Elizabeth Colt Walker for their technical assistance.

The author is indebted to those many boys and girls, parents, babies, medical technicians, physicians, psychologists, nurses and teachers who were so very cooperative and so very patient with him during this study.

All photography in this work is by courtesy of Lloyd Parker Wells, Chestnut Hill, Pa.

CONTENTS

THE TREATMENT AND PREVENTION
OF READING PROBLEMS

1

THE NATURE OF THE RETARDED READER

In the past the teaching of reading has been primarily oral and phonetic in nature; reading was taught after the child knew the sounds of the letters of the alphabet, and the evaluation of mastery of reading was made at an oral level. Until comparatively recently those children who did not learn to read under this system were considered intellectually incapable of reading.

The psychological testing movement gave strong indications that many non-readers had normal capacity or better. Reading specialists then began to analyze the skills involved in reading, and many new techniques were developed. Poor readers have proved tenacious, however, for no matter what techniques were evolved, poor readers stay with us in abundance.

As a result there are many systems for the teaching of reading. Each system has concomitant staunch supporters and each system has severe critics. The criticism and defense of the various systems for the teaching of reading seem fruitless, for with each system some children learn to read and some do not. Historically, when children do not learn to read, the system is modified or changed. The new system helps some children to learn to read but there are always good readers and poor readers, no matter what the system.

These systems fall into three general categories, each with its own bias. There is the *educational bias*. This

3

bias stresses teaching technique from many points of view. There are the progressives, who feel that reading is a process of waiting for ripening and maturity to take place. There are the "phonetic" biased educators who feel that children must learn to read phonetically, and conversely there are the word-sight people who feel that everything is learned from a Gestalt or "whole" concept. There are those who feel that there is too much discipline in education and those who feel that there is not enough discipline. There are those who feel that children should be grouped differently, interested differently and motivated differently. One finds all of these educational facets described in the very abundant educational literature. Many, many books have been written by educators relative to the teaching of reading and remedial reading and yet our poor readers remain with us.

The psychological movement gave us a second bias, *psychologically oriented reading activity.* This bias implies that children should be taught by highly specialized personnel using highly specialized remedial techniques under very favorable "emotional climates." Many children have progressed under such a regime, as did they under the educational regime, but poor readers remain with us.

The third is the *psychiatric bias.* Many investigators have written that children for purely emotional reasons do not learn to read. This bias implies that if we were to solve children's personality and emotional problems, their reading problems would disappear. This has been worked at and written about to a great extent. Our reading and language problems persist.

———

The author joined this fruitless search for a perfect

system. He conducted a series of studies using the various accepted systems as remedial procedures for a period of seven years. The various systems were adapted to the needs of the slow readers. There was growth, but no system proved to be ideal, for with each system there remained the poor readers. Having analyzed the various systems for the teaching of reading, having culled the educational literature, the author concluded that the answer might not lie in the system but might be found elsewhere.

The next step was to cast aside the analysis of the teaching of reading and to make a comprehensive scrutiny of the poor readers themselves, no matter what system was used to teach them, to see if they had common characteristics which could be related to their poor reading.

———

When poor readers are counted on the basis of sex, it is found that the ratio of poor readers is four boys to one girl. Because there are so many more boys than girls, it was decided to analyze forty-five boys who were poor readers. They ranged from eight to eighteen years of age, representing three states and twenty-six very different public, private and parochial schools. The boys were applicants for diagnosis and remediation in a six-week summer reading clinic conducted by the author. For a complete description of the program see: Delacato and Delacato, A Group Approach to Remedial Reading, *Elementary English*, National Council of Teachers of English, Part I, XXIX, No. 3, March, 1952; Part II, XXX, No. 1, January, 1953.

The objective of the analysis was to find how poor readers resemble each other. The criteria were set up as follows: When a trait existed in twenty to thirty boys, it was denoted "fairly common"; in thirty boys or more, "common"; and in over forty, "universal." Any trait which existed in less than twenty boys was discarded as "not common."

The next forty-five boys referred to the clinic were used as the group to be studied. Each boy was diagnosed and taught for at least six weeks, and each characteristic below was evaluated as to its presence or absence in each boy.

Not Common — Fewer than twenty out of the group of forty-five retarded male readers exhibited each of these characteristics, hence, we can assume that if they are causal in poor reading they are not universally causal.

1. Low intelligence
2. Common socio-economic status
3. Race
4. Religion
5. Divorce
6. Very progressive schooling
7. Very conservative schooling
8. Emotional maladjustment
9. Too much phonetic instruction
10. Lack of phonetic instruction
11. Faulty school placement
12. Changing teachers
13. Social immaturity
14. Rigid parents
15. Lax parents
16. Poor in arithmetic
17. Restricted speaking vocabulary
18. Severe emotional conflicts at home
19. Hostility on the part of the child
20. Exhibitionism
21. Poor hearing

22. Poor vision
23. Poor attitude toward school
24. Nail biting
25. Poor present health
26. Lack of interest
27. Lack of motivation
28. Lack of reading materials at home
29. A specific teaching method

The items above have been referred to by teachers, psychologists, and parents as factors which cause poor reading, *yet not one of them was present in twenty or more of the forty-five poor readers.* The author concluded that although each item might be a causal factor in retarding reading for an individual, no single item could be looked to for a general solution to the problems of retarded readers.

The following were titled *Fairly Common* in that they each existed in twenty to thirty of the forty-five poor readers:

1. History of allergies, asthma or choking during the first six years of life.
2. Sibling placement.
3. Hyperactivity in babyhood or childhood.
4. Some early speech slowness or difficulty.

The following were titled *Common* in that each existed in thirty to forty boys in the group of forty-five:

1. Poor penmanship
2. Poor gross coordination
3. Poor manual dexterity
4. Tendency to read or write backwards in the first grade
5. History of a severe childhood illness or head injury

7

The following were titled *Universal* in that each existed in forty or more of the group of forty-five:

1. Early childhood thumbsucking of the thumb on the dominant hand.
2. Posturalization during sleep with the sub-dominant hand prone, or no posturalization.
3. Made a better score on test 5 or 6 (whichever tests the sub-dominant eye) than on test 5 or 6 (whichever tests the dominant eye) on the Telebinocular.
4. Gave some evidence of perceptual confusion in spelling and reading.
5. Some birth complication or longer period of labor than other children in the family.
6. Some lack of unilaterality.
7. Understood and used many more words than he could read.

Upon evaluating the *fairly common, common* and *universal* factors one can easily deduce that these factors seem to be physical or developmental in nature.

The reading pattern of these children showed a very early and consistent history in grades one and two of reversals that is, reading and writing words such as *was* for *saw, on* for *no*, reading and writing numbers such as *24* for *42*. These same children were very poor in early spelling and, if they were fair readers at the time still tended to be poor spellers, reversing letters within words periodically. We found in the reading pattern indications of great difficulty with the word sight method and when the method was changed equally slow mastery of the alphabet or phonetic system. We also found that at all ages these children tended to have higher vocabulary scores than comprehension scores on standardized tests and their reading speed seemed to be very slow. They tended to have significantly more difficulty during early reading years with small words than with large words. Generally they disliked reading. They seemed unable to associate symbols, be they words or sounds, with ideas. They also tended to be good in other academic areas, especially the area of arithmetic. They tended at the secondary school level to have much higher mathematical ability scores than language ability scores on tests of scholastic aptitude. They tended as they went through the junior high and secondary school years to have low marks in English and most of their reading courses but tended to do well in memory courses and courses involving mathematics and mechanical skills.

The next step was to evaluate the area within the physical organism which might be even more specifically related. The area in which all of the forty-five retarded readers had something in common now appeared to be in the *neurological realm*. This premise seemed more valid because the obvious basis of all learning rests within the central nervous system. The premise gains validity when one evaluates the ways in which good readers learn to read. Teaching the good reader to read has never been a problem to educators. No difficulty is encountered in teaching good readers *regardless of the system used to teach them. Good readers seem to learn to read by wholes, indeed by osmosis, and they also exist in every kind of classroom and in every kind of school.*

The author investigated the differences between good readers and poor readers and those differences all pointed toward the neurological realm as the potential etiological factor in poor language and reading development.

9

2

NEUROLOGICAL RESEARCH IN READING

Having ascertained the universal traits of the forty-five retarded readers, it was decided to go back to the literature to see if past research in the field of neurology could be used in solving the problem. There was much data which alluded to a neurological etiology in reading failure, but there was no specific diagnostic or treatment rationale. All of the references pointed back to the original rationale supplied by Samuel Orton, a neurologist who, in 1928, wrote relative to cortical function:

> The first serves to give awareness that a visual sensation comes from without and is not a recalled memory of things seen; in psychologic terms, this level furnishes the element of external awareness in sensation. This function, without such question, resides in the area striata or calcarine cortex of the occipital lobes. The second level, that of objective memories, serves as the storehouse for visual impressions of objects which have been seen. This function probably resides in the second type of occipital cortex which surrounds the calcarine or striate area. Up to this point the two hemispheres of the brain apparently work in unison to produce a single conscious impression; i.e., the messages relayed from the eyes to the two sides of the brain are fused so as to give only one impression. This is brought into relief by the fact that neither of these functions is entirely lost as a result of the destruction of either hemisphere; a bilateral lesion is required to suppress the function of either the first or the second visual platforms. At the third or associative level, however, de-

struction in one hemisphere may result in complete loss of the associative function, resulting in inability to read (acquired word blindness), while destruction of exactly the same area in the opposite hemisphere will not give rise to any symptoms whatever. That hemisphere in which destruction produces loss of the associative function is called the dominant hemisphere, and may be either the left or the right, according to the side which habitually initiates the motor responses of the individual. In other words, it is obvious that the visual records of one side only are used in symbolic association and those of the other are elided or inactive in this process.

Structurally, however, there is no such contrast between the two hemispheres. The non-dominant associative area is as well developed in size and complexity as is the dominant, and current neurologic belief (neurobiotaxis) would imply that this silent or inactive area must have been irradiated equally with the active to produce an equal growth. Such an irradiation, moreover, would presumably leave behind it some record in the cells of the non-dominant side which one may call an "engram". The engram in the non-dominant side would be opposite in "sing", however, from that of the dominant; i.e., it would form a mirrored or anti-tropic pattern. Under usual circumstances only one of these reciprocally paired engrams operates in association with the concept in reading, as is shown by the facts of acquired word blindness already cited, and its antitropic or mirrored mate is elided or remains inoperative. If, however, the physiologic habit of complete elision of these engrams of the non-dominant hemisphere were not established, their persistence might readily serve to explain the failure to differentiate between "p" and "q" and between "was" and "saw", and also to account for facility in mirror reading and mirror writing, and thus to explain those confusions of direction which have been extensively recorded in the literature and which as here described seemed to characterize all the cases of my own series. Since this conception of the disability as a physiologic variant differs so widely from the pathologic moment known to result in acquired word blindness, I have felt that the use of the term "congenital word blindness" was misleading and have offered the the term strephosymbolia—twisted symbols—to demarcate better the series of cases showing this typical symptomology. (Orton, S. T.: Specific Reading Disability-Strephosymbolia. *Journal of the American Medical Association,* April 7, 1928, pp. 1095-1099.)

Orton's was the most widely known early attempt at relating language function to neurological organization. Orton presented very little data toward treatment and none toward prevention of reading problems.

The author then went into the neurological literature to seek other possible answers. He was confused by the great strides made in the field of neurology since Orton's original publications and he was surprised to find much of the data in direct conflict with Orton's rationale. Because he lacked a background in the field, he returned to the fields of education and psychology for help. The leaders in both these fields pleaded ignorance of the field of neurology and implied that a cohesion of education and neurology was impossible. The author then sought out the dean of American neurosurgeons, Dr. Temple Fay, and was privileged to watch, listen to, be taught by and ask questions of Dr. Fay during the years of 1953-1956 in the author's efforts to study the possible relationship of the knowledge of neurology to that of psychology and education. Those three years of study enabled the author to initiate the experimentation which has resulted in the neuropsychological rationale for the treatment and prevention of reading retardation described in this work.

The most recent and most exhaustive survey of the problem is entitled, "Factors Related to Disability in Reading," by Marjorie Seddon Johnson of Temple University, which appears in the *Journal of Experimental Education*, Vol. 26, pp. 1-26, September, 1957.

The article summarizes:

In the past, specific disabilities have been considered traceable to destruction or maldevelopment of brain tissue to loss of certain specialized determinants in the germ plasm, to malfunction of certain brain areas, and to results of birth injuries. Many of these theories arose from comparison with cases of acquired reading disability. Although there are similarities in the two types of cases in that the reading disability seems always to be accompanied by disturbances in other language functions, no one of the theories advanced appears adequate to account for all cases of reading disability.

The article summarizes the area of cortical dominance as follows:

There appears to be adequate evidence that language functions can be disturbed by malfunctioning of certain areas of the brain in the dominant hemisphere, usually the side opposed to the dominant hand. Present inadequate evidence, using tests which make bimanual production of certain patterns, suggests that there may be a positive relationship between confusion in "central" dominance and specific reading disability.

Peripheral Dominance — Ratings of lateral preference in peripheral activities have not always been adequate nor have the investigator's ratings of achievement in reading given adequate attention to level of general capacity. In addition, this factor has sometimes been emphasized unduly because of special interests of the investigators. Only two conclusions seem reliable in view of the limitations of the studies. First, neither hand nor eye preference appears to be, in itself, a significant factor in reading disability. Second, preference for one hand and the opposite eye is probably not a significant factor in itself, but may be indicative of some basic problem.

13

As the Johnson article points out, the causative theories run from Rutherford's, of 1909, who felt that reading disability was the result of a differentiation within germ plasm and could be expected to fall on a normal curve and was genetic in nature; to Rauschburg, who felt that it was the lack of constant blood supply to the language area of the brain; to Orton, who felt that the answer lay not in structure but in function.

Orton's functional rationale is tenable excepting for the concept that visual patterns are stored in the brain. All the evidence we now have in both psychology and neurology negates this concept.

There is no doubt that the current data tends toward a functional rationale. Up to the present, however, none has been forthcoming.

The difficulty remains one of diagnosis. For instance, psychological examination might reveal potential or possible cortical trauma if one analyzes the results of the Wechsler Intelligence Scale for Children, the Koch's Block Test, or the Holmgren Yarn Test. When, however, one refers a patient for neurological evaluation one many times finds that the evaluative results fall within normal limits. Most times those cases in which indications of cortical trauma are found, are those which are fairly obvious and generally exhibit concomitant motor dysfunction. Those cases in which psychological indications of trauma are found, but in which neurological evaluations fall within normal limits are probably those cases which are not traumatic in etiology but are functional (organizational or developmental) in neurological etiology. *These cases are in the great majority, representing 70% of the cases of reading retardation seen by most clinics and these cases are the most difficult simply because there are no real diagnostic techniques for evaluating and testing them.*

14

3

THEORETIC CONSIDERATIONS

The author will discuss the following concepts which form the basis of his rationale for the treatment and prevention of reading and language problems.

A. Man's neurological organization and development ontogenetically recapitulates the phylogenetic development of the nervous system.

B. The basic cortical difference between man and slightly lower forms of animals is not a difference in cellular acquisitions or cellular quantity but is in great part a difference in cellular organization and cellular function. Because man differs from lower forms of animal primarily at a cortical level the way in which the levels are differentiated becomes the reason why man is man and why man has been able to conquer his planet.

C. The evaluation of slight cortical dysfunction or trauma is very difficult, and the evaluation of neurological disorganization is practically impossible with our present tools.

D. The newest cells phylogenetically are those cells which, in part, give man the difference which he has from lower forms of animals (i.e., language). These cells are in instances of trauma the most vulnerable cells that man has acquired. Therefore, the most complex and newest cells, phylogenetically, are the most vulnerable to trauma or to developmental interference. Trauma results in aphasia, i.e., communication distortion.

E. Data indicates that language is controlled at a

15

cortical level in the following way. The dominant side of the cortex controls the skill facets of language, and the subdominant hemisphere controls the tonal facets of language.

F. Phylogenetically the ancient reflexes and their concomitant behavioral indications remain vestigally within man's neuro-muscular and neuro-psychological systems.

G. Man differs neuro-muscularly from lower forms of animals in that he operates in a dominant-sub-dominant pattern. That is, in modern man one side of the cortex takes over most of the skill activity in which man is engaged. This is true for eyedness, footedness and handedness.

H. Cortical localization as an absolute, when dealing with the complexities of language, is invalid. Localization related to language must be made in terms of the *dynamics* of cortical function rather than in terms of specific topological or cellular locations of cortical function. All receptive modalities follow the same pattern and operate as parts of a neurological whole.

I. Peripheral activity or peripheral modalities such as vision, dexterity, skills, phonetics, various reading techniques, are meaningless in remediation if the total neurological organization is defective. The pre-requisite to peripheral therapy is central neurological organization.

————

Historically all of the approaches used for the diagnosis and remediation of reading problems have been peripheral in nature. We have evaluated techniques; we have dealt with various ways of going about teaching reading; both peripheral activities. We have evaluated the children peripherally. We have evaluated their I.Q.'s, we have evaluated their vision, we have evaluated their

16

hearing, we have evaluated their handedness never organizing all that data comprehensively. We must evaluate children at a wholistic level and also treat them at a wholistic level because children don't learn to speak and read in a vacuum, nor do they learn to speak and read with small or specific parts of their minds and bodies. Reading and speaking are part of a whole and hence the author subscribes to a wholistic theory of diagnosis, of treatment and of prevention.

Let us evaluate the peripheral versus the wholistic approach more closely for a moment. We have seen incidences of children who lose the function of the dominant hand at ages six, seven and eight and as a result begin to stutter, stammer and fail in reading. Truly one cannot say that the hand has anything to do directly with reading. Where then lies the answer? The answer of course lies within the cortex where the hand is controlled. The injury is peripheral, and as a result the child adjusts cortically in order to accommodate to his world. The neurological adjustments and the resultant loss in reading ability and language ability are of a wholistic nature. For example, if the child loses the controlling or sighting eye, his reading if he is a six, seven, eight, or nine year old tends to show a very significant loss. In some instances we might even have stuttering and stammering. The eye is of a peripheral nature in this situation, the language changeover is the result of a differential in the cortical dynamics. There, therefore, lies the problem.

These two examples indicate the great need for a wholistic approach. The reading doesn't lie in that eye, it doesn't lie in that arm and yet is affected by those things. Hence in remediation we must finally evolve a wholistic approach. By using the periphery to our advantage to implement our wholistic approach, we can increase language facility.

The author submits this neuro-psychological approach to language function as a preliminary report and as somewhat supportive data toward the new movement of evaluating the reader rather than the technique. Naturally there will be more study and experimentation. The author hopes that other investigators will look into some of these phenomena for he feels that this is a great area for potential investigation. Many of these points need much more experimentation and much more data before final validation.

The author wishes to caution future investigators that this rationale is not aimed at improving intelligence or speeding the evolutionary process but is instead a method for the improvement of the ability to communicate.

4

NEUROLOGICAL ORGANIZATION AND DEVELOPMENT IN POOR READERS

NEUROLOGICAL organization is that physiologically optimum condition which exists uniquely and most completely in man and is the result of a total and uninterrupted ontogenetic neural development. This development recapitulates the phylogenetic neural development of man and begins during the first trimester of gestation and ends at about six and one half years of age in normal humans. This orderly development in humans progresses *vertically* through the spinal cord and all other areas of the central nervous system up to the level of the cortex, as it does with all mammals. Man's final and unique developmental progression takes place at the level of the cortex and it is *lateral* (from left to right or from right to left).

This progression is an *interdependent continuum,* hence if a high level of development is unfunctioning or incomplete, such as in sleep or as the result of trauma, lower levels become operative and dominant (mid-brain sleep and high cervical pathological reflexes). If a lower level is incomplete all succeeding higher levels are affected both in relation to their height in the central nervous system and in relation to the chronology of their development. Man's only contribution to this organizational schema is that he has added to the vertical progression, the final lateral progression at the level of the cortex. Here again, at the cortical level, the same premises apply.

The final progression must become dominant and must supersede all others. Prerequisite, however, to such dominance is the adequate development of all lower levels.

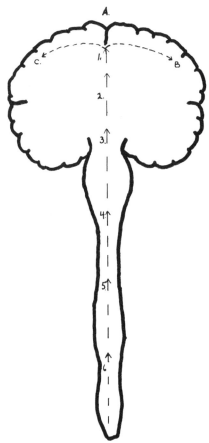

FIGURE 1. Neuro-organizational schema (posterior view). A. Point to which animals slightly lower phylogenetically than man can arrive. B. Point to which totally developed left-sided human arrives. C. Point to which totally developed right-sided human arrives. Numbers denote lower neural levels which affect higher levels and which are in turn affected by higher levels. Upon failure of a higher level the next lower level becomes dominant.

20

In totally developed man the left or the right cortical hemisphere must become dominant, with lower prerequisite requirements met, if his organization is to be complete *(see Figure 1).*

Phylogenetics is the study of the evolution of man. Phylogenetically the nervous system has evolved from a very simple to a very complex mechanism. As evolution progressed, animals achieved what could be compared to a spinal cord. These animals operated chiefly at a reflex level. As time went on in the evolutionary cycle, the mid-brain was developed, and finally there evolved animals which operated slightly under the level of man, who has a cortex. Through the evolutionary cycle man has developed a cortex, yet vestigally he retains the lower level neurological appendages and functions which were needed during this developmental cycle. If the animals which operate slightly under the level of man are analyzed, they are found to have a cortex. Generally they have the neuro-anatomical structure of man but these animals cannot do the following things: stand fully upright, see three dimensionally, oppose the thumb and forefinger, supinate and pronate the hand, speak or write a language and, operate unilaterally with the hand, foot and eye of one side of the body.

The neurological differences between man and slightly lower forms of animals are not cellularly important. The basic difference between man and the animal world is that man has achieved cortical dominance wherein one side of the cortex controls the skills in which man outdistances lower forms of animals. This whole phylogenetic process is recapitulated ontogenetically with each human being. In the event that there is some obstruction to this ontogenetic recapitulation, communication and language dysfunctions occur.

Man has evolved to the point that the two hemispheres of the brain, although they mirror each other physically, have differentiated functions. Right handed humans are one sided, i.e., they are right eyed, right footed and right handed, with the left cortical hemisphere controlling the organism.

Trauma of the controlling cortical hemisphere results in loss of language skills, but equally important, trauma of the subdominant area results in loss of tonal factors. Left hemiplegics (right handed people who have suffered a cerebrovascular accident to the right or subdominant hemisphere of the cortex) have no difficulty with speech but suffer a very significant loss in tonal memory, tonal appreciation and the ability to carry a tune. Generally, their melody, rhythm and accent abilities are affected.

Some investigators feel that man's supremacy is not the result of cellular acquisitions within the cortex but is instead the result of the specialization of function which man has evolved in the use of his cortex. They feel that as man evolved into an ideating and communicating human being, he simultaneously developed cortical laterality. These investigators will tend to feel that the rationale contained herein is not aimed at language but is aimed at increasing man's efficiency in using those modalities which have already made him supreme. Carried to the extreme such a rationale might lead one to conclude that the neuro-psychological approach is not a language function but is instead the method for improving man's position of supremacy, i.e., intelligence. He might conclude that the methods described herein would be significant in the ontogenetic improvement of intelligence.

The author does not concur with this bias. He cautions the reader that the rationale is aimed at improving communication functions and not basic intelligence. Any seeming improvement in intelligence, on the part of children with whom this rationale is used consistently, must be related to increased communication and expressive facility and should not be related to improved intelligence; at least in light of the present data.

Ontogenetics is the study of the development of an individual. The ontogenetic development of the neuro-language function in children in general recapitulates the phylogenetic development and can be outlined as follows:

Children at birth are tonal in nature. They use only vowels in their crying, cooing or vocalizing, consonants are only accidentally produced. A striking factor about new babies is their tendency to be left handed in choice of grasping and use of hand. Thirty years ago ninety-five per cent of our population was right handed; today approximately eighty-five per cent of our population is right handed. To what can we ascribe this tendency on the part of infants to use or to prefer the left hand? Gesell in his clinical studies found this odd characteristic on the part of children and reported it.

Children tend to remain somewhat ambidextrous until about the age of six and a half at which time a dominant hand and foot and eye become established. At this time children are taught the most complex language function, reading. We can all assume that education over many years has found that children are therefore neurologically ready as well as intellectually, socially and emotionally ready to read at about this age.

Now let us retrace our steps on these two functions; that of handedness and that of tonality. As is well known in dealing with people who have cortical damage, if the cortex on the side opposite the side of the body which is the dominant side is damaged (the dominant cortical hemisphere), we find a condition called aphasia or the inability to communicate. These people are unable to speak and to read. One of the well known techniques for helping such people to regain functional speech is using tonality. Although these people have damage in what is the dominant hemisphere of the cortex (the skill side), the subdominant side remains intact and in this area tonality finds its basis. If one takes such a patient and asks him to sing a familiar song, one finds that he can speak all of the words of the tune, can sing such songs as "Happy Birthday to You" and say his own name in it as long as he is singing. When the song is over, he is unable to say his name. The only conclusion we can reach is that the tonality carried the skill section, tonality being in the nonaffected area or subdominant hemisphere.

Now let us evaluate our evidence. First of all, new babies tend to be left handed, yet eighty-five per cent of our population is right handed. In essence the babies are using what will become the subdominant hand. We must remember that most of them will be right handed adults; hence, although these babies are using their subdominant hand, the tonal area or the subdominant area is the area which is being used at this stage of development because their language expression is purely tonal in nature. As they develop skill in language, the tonal expressiveness decreases; as skill is used in phonation and speech, unilateral handedness appears. Concurrently the dominant area of the cortex should become the controlling cortical hemisphere. The patient who, through damage to the cortex on the dominant side, loses language function including reading and yet can say and remember his name in song, exhibits all of the symptoms of the retarded reader. The tendencies to reverse and to have great associative difficulty in reading are the most conspicuous of these symptoms.

The natural concomitant of the tonal factors should be the elimination of any tonality within the reading situation. If we are to establish a dominant hemisphere, which is the skilled hemisphere, we must put every effort into making the other hemisphere subdominant. We should, therefore, delete all tonal activity in remedial teaching. Reading should be done only in stage whispers. These children should not be asked to read orally other than to whisper the words. This activity tends to increase skill and to activate the dominant or skill hemisphere of the cortex while deactivating the subdominant or tonal hemisphere. By so doing we increase the possibility of gaining unilaterality.

We all have heard of the many cases of stuttering which do not stutter when singing. Music teachers have been historically amazed with this phenomenon. The author feels that the stuttering is the result of too much hemispheric balance. There is no dominance, hence we have a stutter. If we add tonality, the hemisphere which controls tonality and which is normally the subdominant hemisphere becomes dominant and the stutter disappears. During the remedial period an additional tonal consideration is present. This is the overall consideration of listening to and making music. Children going through such a remedial program first of all should not listen to music and secondly should not sing. All this is an effort to preclude any unnecessary use and therefore activation of the subdominant area. This is made necessary by the fact that dominance has not been established and we want to use every activity to our avail to establish such dominance.

Remedial activity therefore should be silent on the part of the reader; and all oral reading should be done from a skill point of view, using whispers only. As many tonal activities, both receptive and expressive, as is possible should be *deleted* from the child's environment until dominance of the skilled hemisphere of the cortex has been established.

5

SLEEP AS IT RELATES TO READING

THEORIES concerning sleep are numerous. They seem to be especially plentiful in the area of childhood sleep. They usually fall into three categories:

1. Body Heat
2. Fluid Level
3. Body Position

The factor of body heat is very relevant. All schools of thought on child care indicate that body heat must be kept within a certain range if sleep is to be maintained. During sleep blood pressure decreases, heart rate decreases, breathing rate decreases, temperature decreases, oxygenation decreases; all activities typical of the amphibian stage of phylogenetic development. Data on amphibians includes each of the above as descriptive of the amphibian and comparative anatomy corroborates the amphibian as operating with a brain which remains vestigally with man as his old brain or midbrain.

Fluid regulation is still used to induce sleep. Still in general credence is the statement that when the fontanel of the baby is convex or bulging the baby will sleep and that when it is concave the baby will be restless unless fed. If one takes a baby with a concave fontanel and concomitant restlessness and feeds him a bottle, one finds that the cerebro-spinal fluid increases, the fontanel becomes convex, and the baby falls asleep. Indeed, as the child sleeps and the fluid level decreases, one finds that the baby pushes the top of its head into a corner of its crib or pushes the top of its head against the covers, a soft toy or a pillow to gain an increased pressure in the cerebro-spinal system. This cerebro-spinal system is a double and communicating system, composed of the internal and the external systems. The internal system consists of the two lateral ventricles, their foramina of Monro, the third ventricle, the fourth ventricle, and the aqueduct of Sylvius. The external system consists of the subarachnoid spaces, including the dilated areas known as the cisterns. These two systems form a closed system with a direct relation between volume and pressure. Both volume and pressure changes are directly communicated through the foramina of Luschka, found in the lateral recesses of the fourth ventricle, and the foramen of Magendie, found in the roof of the fourth ventricle.

Historically, mothers have put their babies to sleep with the tops of their heads gently pushed into a pillow because babies tend to seek this position and tend to sleep better and longer in this position. The phylogenetic stage at which the greatest adjustment to external-internal pressure was necessary was obviously the amphibious stage, with both air and water as immediate pressure environments. No other phylogenetic level presented more than one type of pressure environment; the only exception was the mid-brain or amphibious level, the same level in which man sleeps.

If one observes children closely, one sees a striking developmental pattern. Infants tend to assume amphibian level serialized postural reflexes pre-natally, and post-natally for both rest and reaction. Gesell [*] describes this reactive pattern as follows:

> The four-week-old infant when awake lies on his back with his head averted, usually to a preferred side. Only

[*] Gesell, Arnold, et al.: The First Five Years of Life. Harper and Brothers, New York, 1940, pp. 18-19, 21.

momentarily does he bring his head to a mid position. Almost invariably his arm is extended on the side toward which his head is turned. The opposite arm is flexed with the hand resting near or in the head-chest region. The combination of averted head, extended arm, and flexed arm is the so-called tonic-neck-reflex attitude (t.n.r.) which dominates the waking life of the infant for some twelve weeks.

Occasionally the four-week-old infant bursts into startle responses, his head coming momentarily to the mid-line and all his extremities extending abruptly. Occasionally he lashes the air with more or less symmetric windmill movements of the arms. But the asymmetric t.n.r. attitude underlies most of his postural behavior. Indeed, the t.n.r. is part of the ground plan of the total reaction system. In partial form it was present prenatally, helping the fetus to accommodate to the outlines of the uterine cavity. At 16 weeks it gives way to more symmetric patterns of behavior, but it is a precondition for the growth of these later patterns.

At sixteen weeks "the t.n.r. is losing its sway" continues Gesell, "but during its ascendency it serves to channelize the pathways of visual attention. It led by gradual stages from diffuse and fleeting fixations on the extended arm to prolonged inspection of the hand."

The generally accepted concept has been that the tonic neck reflex disappears rapidly after sixteen weeks and that it only reoccurs as a pathological reflex when higher centers are damaged.

The author has demonstrated that this is an erroneous conclusion because it dealt with only the supine position and while the subject was awake. When children are evaluated prone and asleep (today most children sleep on their stomachs) it is still present and it is the author's opinion that the tonic neck reflex and what it connotes in terms of total neurological organization, with its important implications for language, is a critical factor in the evaluation, treatment and prevention of language disabilities.

If a new-born is placed in a supine position and his head is turned either right or left, there follows a reflex rotation of the spine in the direction of the head rotation. If the pelvis is held fixed, the shoulder girdle and trunk follow the head, if the thorax is held fixed, the pelvis is turned in the opposite direction. If the reflex is strong, the turning of the head leads to a violent turning of the body as a whole in the direction of the head rotation. All of these movements are efficient and spontaneous and all are *serialized*.

Complex serialized reflexes can exist under a modified functional schemata brought about by an assimilative process. Piaget [*] feels that reflex patterns form the basis for intelligence and through use they are reinforced, and because of the development of higher levels of accommodations they are assimilated. The author agrees that they do not disappear but are instead assimilated.

The author feels that disappearance of the tonic neck reflex as a functional aspect of behavior is further negated through the observation of a number of people of all ages during supine sleep. Those who sleep in the supine position assume the same postural patterns as those who sleep in the prone position but the positions are reversed. Although reversed, the posturalization *patterns* remain intact.

If one takes a child in prone and patterned sleep and turns his head in the opposite direction, one finds that the complete body organization reverses itself. *See Figures 2, 3 and 4.*

If this reversal does not take place, the normal reading

_____
[*] Piaget, Jean: *The Origins of Intelligence in Children.* International Universities Press, Inc., New York, 1952, page 32.

child awakens. *Both these movements take place in good readers only.* (It is probably a serialized reflex of ancient phylogenetic origin wherein the turning of the head with the body in the prone position induces the limbs toward which the face is turned to flex and the opposite limbs to extend. All this is vestigal from the amphibious level, when this serialized reflex pattern was used for propulsive purposes.)

The author feels that the reason that poor readers do not sleep in such a position and if put in such a position will not awaken, if the tonic neck reflex does not take place, is because of a lack of organization which prevents the serialization required in this pattern. Poor readers have all of the component reflexes and skills required for the reflex, but their neuro-muscular systems are not organized so that the serialization of the various neural components can take place.

This helps to explain at least in part why poor readers are found by many investigators to seem uncoordinated in running, jumping, walking and writing. This ancient serialized reflex continues as partially functional in man. Man walks upright because of it. If one analyzes the origin of walking, it proceeds as follows: Standing upright and balanced, the individual is stable but immobile. As a visual stimulus catches the attention, and both eyes focus on the stimulus, the head turns toward it; and the neck must follow in the motion, setting off the serialized tonic neck reflex. As a result of this the limbs toward which the face is turned flex, the limbs on the opposite side extend, and a balanced step is taken. Poor readers seem incoordinated in that they are unable because of a lack of neural organization to take advantage of the neural efficiency which serialization contributes to the pattern. They can accomplish all the movements but they cannot serialize them. Serialization makes for coordina-

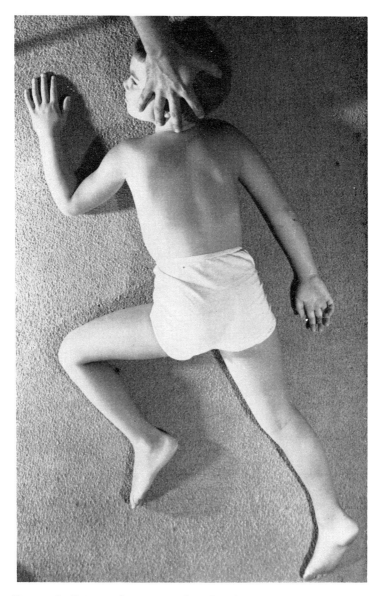

Figure 2. Prior to the tonic neck reflex the figure is at rest facing the left hand which is prone. The left arm and leg are flexed.

FIGURE 3. As the head is turned and the tonic neck reflex begins
to take place the postural attitude of the entire body changes. As
the trunk meets the mid-point the flexed limbs begin to extend.
Note also the beginning of supination of the left hand and the
beginning of pronation of the right hand.

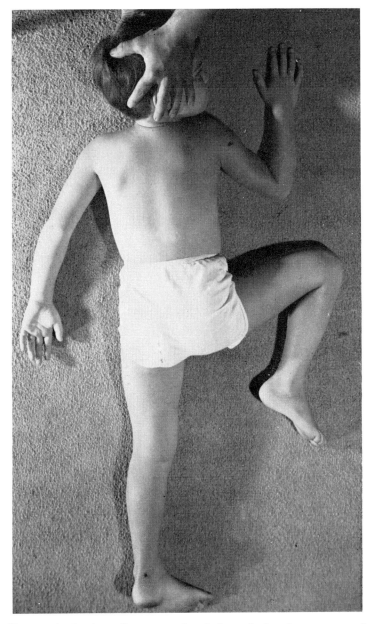

FIGURE 4. As the reflex is completed the right hand pronates and the right arm and leg flex, the opposite limbs extend. The figure has completed the serialized pattern and is at rest.

tion, hence poor readers seem unable to coordinate at both a gross and fine muscle level.

If one analyzes neural organization, one can readily understand the relationship of body position in sleep to total neurological organization. Let us analyze this at its most superficial level; for if it follows at this level, the implications at deeper levels are even greater and more relevant. Let us analyze the various levels of cutaneous innervation. When one analyzes a standing or outstretched prone human in these terms one finds a confused picture of innervation. The picture indicates that Mother Nature, the most orderly of concepts, was grossly confused and disorganized in setting up the human neural anatomy. One has difficulty, especially with arm and leg innervation, actually ascertaining any pattern for cutaneous innervation. *See Figures 5 and 6.*

If one positions the same human being in a quadruped position, however, one sees that Mother Nature has essentially a magnificent order about her. In a changed position, therefore, one can easily ascertain levels of innervation and the whole system is well ordered and logical. *See Figure 7.*

The author feels that only with a proper posturalization basis can the organism achieve the more complex neuro-muscular unity and organization required by cortically controlled accommodations. He feels that such unity is pre-requisite to skilled cortically controlled sensory-motor functions which operate in a wholistic and serialized pattern. He further feels that such unity is pre-requisite to the development of efficiency of communication. Proper posturalization in the prone position (these patterns are also relevant in the supine position but are reversed) is as follows:

1. The eyes looking toward the subdominant hand.

34

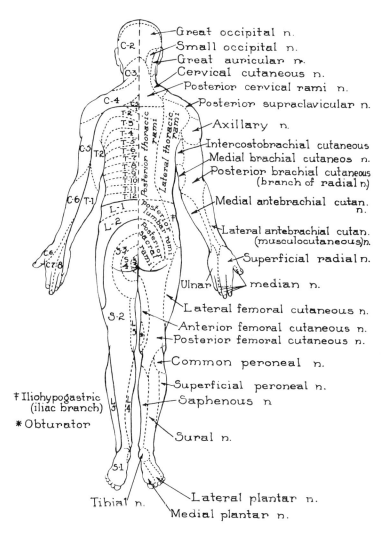

FIGURE 5. Cutaneous innervation (posterior view). Figures 5, 6 and 7 from McDonald and Chusid's Correlative Neuroanatomy and Functional Neurology, 6th Ed., 1952. Courtesy of Lange Medical Publications, Los Altos, California.

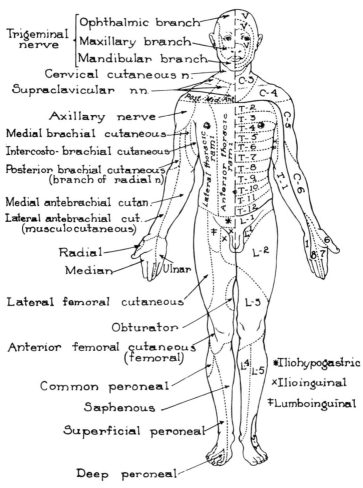

Trigeminal nerve
- Ophthalmic branch
- Maxillary branch
- Mandibular branch

Cervical cutaneous n.
Supraclavicular nn.
Axillary nerve
Medial brachial cutaneous
Intercosto-brachial cutaneous
Posterior brachial cutaneous (branch of radial n)
Medial antebrachial cutan.
Lateral antebrachial cut. (musculocutaneous)
Radial
Median — Ulnar
Lateral femoral cutaneous
Obturator
Anterior femoral cutaneous (femoral)
Common peroneal
Saphenous
Superficial peroneal
Deep peroneal

*Iliohypogastric
×Ilioinguinal
‡Lumboinguinal

FIGURE 6. Cutaneous innervation (anterior view).

2. The arm and leg flexed on the side which the child is facing.
3. The opposite (dominant) arm and leg extended.
4. The hand near the mouth (subdominant) should be palm down with the thumb pointing to the mouth.

36

5. The extended hand (dominant) should be palm up and near the hip.
See Figures 8, 9, 10 and 11.

To recapitulate, we find that children who are poor readers either do not have a sleep pattern or have a faulty sleep pattern. *See Figures 12 and 13.* We find that good readers do have a specific sleep pattern. In this pattern the good reader sleeps facing the subdominant hand with the subdominant leg flexed. *See Figures 8, 9, 10 and 11.*

We find a lack of neurological organization in obvi-

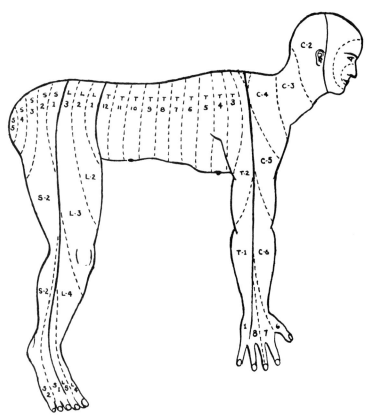

Figure 7. Cutaneous innervation in the quadruped position.

37

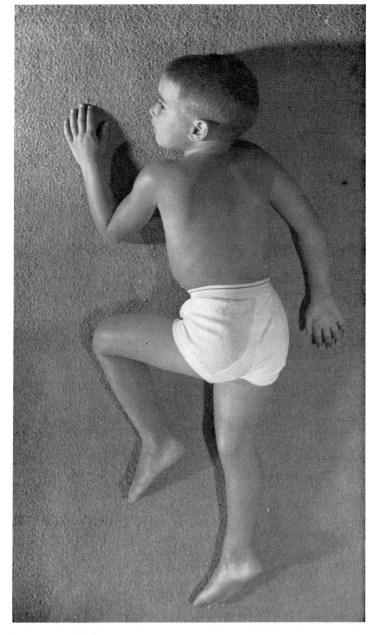

FIGURE 8. Ideal sleep pattern for very young children who have indicated a right sided preference.

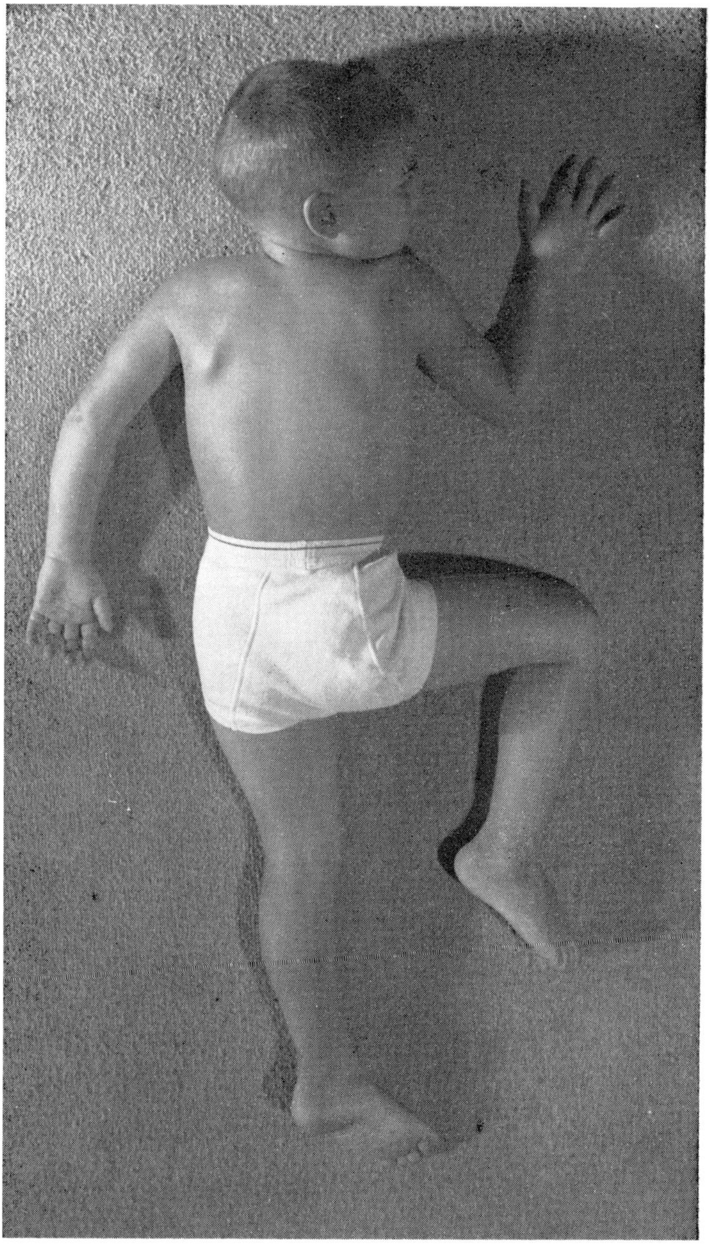

FIGURE 9. Ideal sleep pattern for very young children who have indicated a left sided preference.

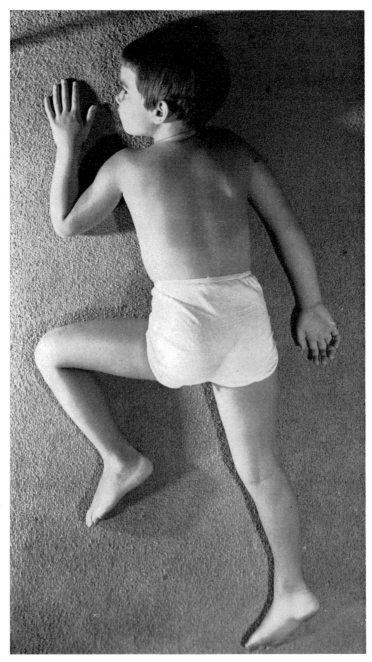

FIGURE 10. Ideal sleep pattern for a right handed child who is neurologically well organized for beginning reading. Note the greater postural relaxation in this age child as compared with the relaxation of the younger child in Figures 8 and 9.

FIGURE 11. Ideal sleep pattern for a left handed child who is neurologically well organized for beginning reading.

FIGURE 12. Confused sleep pattern of a younger child which is indicative of inadequate neurological organization.

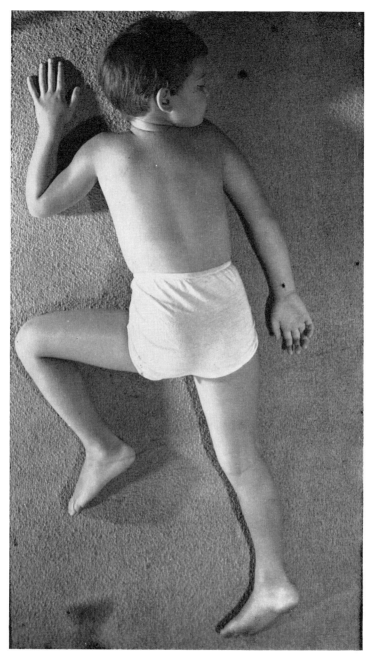

FIGURE 13. Confused sleep pattern of a school age child which is indicative of inadequate neurological organization and is also indicative of potential reading difficulties.

ously brain injured children, such as in cerebral palsy, and in brain injured adults, such as in stroke cases or in traumatic brain injuries. If we accept the rationale from a developmental point of view and the data of the original study (see page 8), the only alternative is to teach the children to posturalize in sleep. The author has found that posturalization in sleep is an important pre-requisite to corrective remedial measures. He also suggests that as a preventive measure as part of early childhood care, mothers be taught to posturalize their children in sleep in an effort to further neurological organization and to assure neurological unity as the child begins to develop its first skilled language activities.

Further investigation of children with even slight remedial reading problems indicates that they do not posturalize or that they posturalize incorrectly during sleep (such as by posturalizing with the dominant hand prone and by using the subdominant hand to play with the blanket or to effect early childhood explorative movements). We find that these same children tend, as they grow older, to suck the thumb of the dominant hand and to continue the exploratory or security seeking type of activity such as blanket rubbing or teddy bear holding with the subdominant hand. As can be recalled, both sleeping on the stomach and thumb sucking were not allowed twenty years ago but in light of the new data we have on the psychology of childhood development both these activities are now tolerated and indeed condoned in the child development literature. Hence we might well be, in part, creating reading problems which might not have become problems had those children not gone through these two experiences.

6

BRAIN INJURIES AND POOR READING

THE evidence indicates that boys have reading problems in a four to one ratio to girls. We know that under gross trauma, such as a lack of oxygen (hypoxia or anoxia), the brain cells which are newest in the evolutionary scale are the most easily damaged. We know that these most vulnerable cells are highly involved with the phylogenetically recent process of association. Birth statistics indicate that boys heads are larger at birth than are the heads of girls. It would possibly follow that with boys, therefore, the birth process would be more difficult or that the period between leaving the dependence of the mother and beginning breathing would be longer with boys than with girls. If there were some anoxia present, the highest level cells would be damaged first. The other cells might not be affected at all.

The author believes that the child with a severe reading problem might possibly have suffered some anoxia and hence brain damage either during birth or subsequent to it. The obstetrical literature is rapidly supplying more data in this area. Obstetricians are not only cognizant of the classical symptoms of anoxia at birth but are making great strides in prevention. Where body discoloration was formerly the indication for anti-anoxia measures, now very slight discolorations of the fingertips, ears and the nose are ample indications for anti-anoxic procedures. Studies are being made of the intra-uterine oxygen level during birth as a potential preventive measure of anoxia even of a very slight degree.*

As is well known, the lack of oxygen to a human being for a period of three minutes reduces it to a breathing and alive but totally intellectually incapacitated organism because many cortical cells are destroyed through the lack of oxygen. It is also a well established fact that the newest cells phylogenetically (which are the cells dealing with association and language) are the most vulnerable to anoxia.

The question naturally arises: What happens after one minute of oxygen deficiency? The author feels that one minute of anoxia is not enough in most cases to result in the gross motor and intellectual disabilities which are classical symptoms of anoxia but that it is enough to cause some damage to those most vulnerable cells involved with language and association. We know from the obstetrical literature that, generally, first children and boys' births are slower than are second deliveries or girls' births. This could explain why first children and boys seem the most prone to have reading problems. This seems to be a premise which could help to explain why four times as many boys than girls have reading problems. This also explains the great similarity between the language symptoms of the obviously brain injured child and the child with the severe reading problems.

We also know that man has become increasingly dependent on his cortex for all human activity. He has even become dependent on the cortex for activity which was formerly at a sub-cortical level.

In man, the development of the cerebral cortex has led to an inhibition of the activity of the sub-cortical

* For a recent and authoritative treatment of these problems see Wilson, Beecham, Forman and Carrington: *Obstetrics and Gynecology.* C. V. Mosby Company, St. Louis, Mo., 1958.

center, i.e., brain stem, cerebellum, mid-brain and basal ganglia. These centers have lost their autonomy and have been relegated to the background of human motor activity. In the process of evolution man has become increasingly dependent on intact cortical function for the maintenance of upright posture in standing and walking and for the complex activities of arms and legs in prehension and skilled movements. A lesion of the brain of man will therefore result in greater helplessness than will a comparable lesion in an animal.

This holds true as one descends the phylogenetic scale. It has been experimentally demonstrated, for instance, that when dogs and cats are brain damaged thalamically they continue to be able to walk, but when a monkey is brain damaged thalamically he becomes quite unable to walk.

The author has examined more than two hundred brain injured children with concomitant motor dysfunction who were classified as aphasics. The clinical symptomatology of these children relative to spoken language was basically the same as the symptomatology of the retarded reader relative to written language. They differ primarily in degree.

Recognizing the slightly brain injured child is an extremely difficult procedure. This is a universal difficulty. Lewis, Straus and Lehtinen,[*] in a book about brain damaged children state:

> So little is understood about the physiology of the brain that the otherness of the other child (brain injured child) cannot be described with any degree of exactness in physiological terms. If he is not crippled, and in many cases he is not, the brain injury cannot be detected by a medical examination and an electro or pneumoencephalo-

[*] Lewis, Straus, and Lehtinen: *The Other Child.* Grune and Stratton, Inc., New York, 1951, page 3.

gram may not show it. Rather it becomes manifest in the general behavior and intellectual peculiarities of the child which become increasingly conspicuous as he grows older. He may or may not be intellectually retarded. He may simply exhibit pronounced behavior difficulties which do not yield to the usual psychotherapeutic methods. Brain injured children who have reached school age without being recognized as such are frequently found in classes for the mentally defective or in classes for children with behavior problems or struggling and misunderstood in classes for normal children.

And these are the children, the children in classes for normal children, who are not doing well especially in the language area who resemble the brain injured child, to whom we must look.

We must digress for a moment to consider those cases which are of a purely traumatic etiology. Behaviorly these cases are typified by hyper-activity and a tendency toward inattention. Quite often these cases are diagnosed through the typical neurological evaluation. Obviously such problems must be dealt with medically. The entire program for such problems should be controlled and supervised by proficient medical personnel. In such instances the trauma must be counteracted prior to successful remediation. Now let us examine a few such avenues of medical approach.

Method A — We have found that in certain instances children who were unable to learn to read and had all of the traumatic indications outlined above tended to improve significantly under a program of medication which included some tranquilizing agent. Such medication tended to help the patient to pay greater attention, to be less hyper-active and, in so doing, tended to make the patient more receptive to instruction.

For example: Boy D, age seven, a student in an excellent school, was unable to learn to read. His teachers complaints were constant hyper-activity, inattention, lack of interest and general lack of cooperation. Physiologically, D was a fairly well coordinated boy, did well socially, but seemed to be somewhat immature emotionally. Following a complete evaluation, it was a fairly tenable theory that D suffered some traumatic injury. D was then put on a medication program of a tranquilizer and phenobarbital. One week after D's medication was initiated his reading began to improve, his attention increased, his hyper-activity decreased and his general demeanor within the classroom was much improved.

Six months of the medication and the neuro-psychological approach proved sufficient, for D was right up to grade level in his reading and became successful in class. After the six months the medication was gradually diminished and eliminated. Although D became slightly more hyper-active after the medication ceased, this symptom no longer interfered with his schooling to the degree that it did originally, because he had already acquired the skills necessary for success. Having acquired the skills, he could now lose himself in the mastery of content, the appreciation of reading and greater enjoyment of educational activities.

Method B — It was found that severely traumatized central nervous system patients tend to react better when their carbon dioxide retention is increased. Such patients as severely spastic athetoid cerebral palsies tend to lose much spasticity if they are given more carbon dioxide than is usually retained in normal breathing. Such patients during sleep (during which there is an increased retention of carbon dioxide) lose much of their spasticity. The following was tried with one child who gave every indication at a behavioral and an E.E.G. level of being a traumatic injury. A disposable oxygen mask was placed over his face so that no air could circumvent it. The only way in which air could be inhaled was through the small tube type opening which is normally attached to the oxygen tank; hence the child was rebreathing much of the air which he had already exhaled. As a result the oxygen content decreased, and the carbon dioxide content increased. This procedure was followed two minutes per hour in one minute periods during the pre-remedial period.

This boy had previously found no success with remedial reading but, during this program, showed a significant increase in his ability to read and, following six months of remediation at one hour per day, had achieved a nine month growth in reading. Theoretically this was the result of increased carbon dioxide content at a cortical level which is a well known chemo-physiological aid to the cortex's making better use of the oxygen which was supplied. This procedure also tended to decrease hyperactivity during the period immediately following the increased carbon dioxide retention and tended to decrease inattentiveness and the general inability to concentrate.

Method C — The cerebro-spinal canal, as is well known, is a closed fluid system. There seems to be a tendency on the part of people who have had cortical trauma to drink more water per day than do those people who do not have traumatic injury. This phenomenon was observed at first with children who were physically disabled because of traumatic brain injury and was followed through on those children who, although not physically disabled, gave clinical indications of trauma. Chances are that if there were trauma of the cortex (and the resultant dissipation through body organisms of the traumatized area or the resultant formation of scar tissue at the traumatized area) fluids would tend to be absorbed into the cerebro spinal system from the body, such fluids taking the place of actual tissue. Such a situation would naturally cut down the supply of vascular nutriment to the cortex. The cerebro-spinal-fluid weight upon the cortex would displace oxygen-carrying blood in the vessels immediately surrounding the area of trauma (see page 27).

We observed that people with clinically observable traumatic cortical injury tend to drink more water, and secondly we observed that cutting down their fluid intake tended to decrease incidences of seizures and tended to decrease hyper-activity. A study was made of the effectiveness of such a program on children who have traumatic injury of a lesser degree. Upon investigation it was found that these children tend to learn reading better during hot weather than they do during typical cool schooltime weather. Children who worked in the summertime also tended to make more progress in reading than they did in the winter. The three factors mentioned above related to cerebro-spinal-fluid and pressure were taken into consideration and were made operative in the following case history.

Boy M — age nine, did not speak, could not relate to any human being and was perfectly well physically except that he had a slight ataxic gait. Although age nine he had been unable to learn to speak, read, communicate and could barely follow directions. Because his parents and medical and psychological personnel had deemed him uneducable and untrainable, he was to be sent to an institution for life. In light of the great problems which he presented, an experimental approach to his problems was accepted by medical, psychological personnel and parents. The child gave all the symptoms of being a potential cerebro-spinal problem. He was put on a program of thirty ounces of fluids per day, a program of neurological organization, and a program of general socio-educational orientation. The results were dramatic. In eight weeks the child, although he had lost a great deal of weight, had learned many words, could carry on a rudimentary conversation, could follow directions at a two step level, was much calmer, was able to deal in symbolic language in a significantly better way. This same boy had received many other types of treatment with absolutely no effect.

Now let us look at another case. Boy X, age fourteen, was a cerebral palsied child from birth. Boy X had an I.Q. of one hundred and tended to be able to learn arithmetic, social graces, get along with other people and enjoy television, but he could not learn to read. Having cut down on his fluid intake for a period of six weeks, the program of neurological organization was initiated. In combination the boy learned to read at a fifth grade level and was able to go back to his special school and to compete with his former classmates.

Naturally the programs outlined above must be supervised by proper medical personnel. Having worked out a medical program to counteract whatever behavioral and receptive difficulties we have as the result of trauma, the physician can then turn the child over to a program which uses a neuro-organizational approach to the learning of reading.

The author wishes to caution the reader at this point that in his experience with retarded readers *barely 30% could be classified as traumatic in etiology.* The others fell into the developmental-organizational category. Although the rationale described in this work fits the traumatic group (following proper medical care), it is aimed at the remaining 70%, who heretofore have defied both diagnosis and remediation. The reason that usual neurological evaluations have not isolated these factors in the past is obvious. Neurologists are concerned primarily with nervous system problems which have an extrinsic effect on human activity. The Babinsky and Marie-Foix reflexes are not indicative because they exist transiently in very young children. The E.E.G. loses much of its value as a diagnostic technique because of the great overlap of normal and abnormal E.E.G.'s. Indeed, therefore, the only area in which one can perceive either a slight trauma or a developmental problem is in the area of behavior. Developmental neurology is a very new and at present somewhat academic area of investigation. The author feels it to be an extremely important area for increased future investigation.

7

HANDEDNESS AND FOOTEDNESS AS THEY RELATE TO READING

THE historical background of left handedness or ambidexterity is interesting. The word sinister means left handed. The word gauche means left handed. During medieval days left handers were considered potential court jesters. Religion takes cognizance of handedness as is well known in the Catholic religious procedure. Leonardo da Vinci knew no Greek or Latin. People accused him of witchcraft and heresy because of his secret writings. Although he could not learn what others could learn such as Latin and Greek, the brilliance of his mind was obvious. Upon being accused of heresy da Vinci absolved himself with a mirror. He was a reversing writer. His drawings were many times done backwards, with a mirror they were recognizable. As a result he was absolved of the accusation of heresy. da Vinci was ambidextrous, he could write with both hands but could not read well.

Today we are more accepting of left handedness, hence today fifteen per cent of our population, as compared with 5 to 8% in 1920, is left handed. Schools no longer force all children to be right handed. We have gone so far as to have refrigerators and doors which are left handed. Teachers are urged not to do anything about handedness. *Perhaps we have gone too far.* True we should not set up a situation wherein we train a child toward a sidedness which is non-acceptable to him in terms of genetic bias. By the same token, however, we must be constantly aware of the need for unilaterality, that dynamic aspect of neurological organization which distinguishes man from lower animals.

Children should be observed carefully from infancy in terms of laterality. Most infants tend to use the left hand more than the right. At about the age of one year to 18 months this usually changes. At this point 85% of children should begin to use the right hand as the preferred hand, but not as the only hand. At this point the child is ambidextrous but has a preferred hand. From this time on he should be encouraged to use the preferred hand for *all activities and ambidexterity should be discouraged.* The writer cautions that about 15% of the population will prefer to use the left hand at this time. *They should be encouraged to use the left hand and ambidexterity should be discouraged.* Although at this age children have not established a dominant hand, they should be helped to develop the preferred hand into the dominant hand through suggestion and teaching.

From this age on unilaterality or single handedness should be encouraged. It should be encouraged during the pre-school years because of the many related factors. For example: If one watches children of three and four drawing or cutting with scissors, one can readily observe that the eye on the same side as the hand being used is the sighting eye for these activities. *The early acquisition of a dominant hand biases the organism toward the establishment of proper visual dominance.*

In dealing with the retarded reader the ascertainment of handedness should proceed as follows: First, one finds a choice of handedness in the history. Secondly, one hands many objects to the patient, checking to see which hand is used. Thirdly, one can ask the child to cut something with a scissors, pick something up, point to something. There are obviously many techniques for the ascertainment of the dominant hand. One can also use a finger grip test for each hand and will find that usually the dominant hand is the stronger gripping hand. Again it must be stated neither left handedness nor right handedness is preferable, the only real objective is unilaterality; *all right handedenss or all left handedness.*

To ascertain footedness one has the subject stand feet together and asks the subject to take a step forward, backward, sideways. He should ask the subject to kick a ball. This test is somewhat invalid because it is mitigated against by many educational activities such as learning certain games, learning to march or learning to dance. The test described above can give only a fairly reliable index of footedness.

Case history: Boy R had a great deal of difficulty with reading, he reversed *was* for *saw*, *on* for *no*, *dog* for *god* and to complicate matters was an implosive stutterer. Boy R had many problems of an emotional nature as a result of his inability to read and his stuttering. Quite accidentally Boy R broke his sub-dominant arm at the age of seven. After the arm had been in a cast for five weeks, a noticeable difference came over the young man. His stuttering disappeared, and the reading symptoms tended to become negligible. As a result the young man did well at school following that time, and his emotional adjustments were immediately improved.

The author does not suggest that we immobilize the arms of children who have laterality problems but does suggest that we, through education, teach children to be unilateral. Indeed the author has had remarkable success with a few children who represent that very difficult group of three to four to five year old non-talkers. With those children he has literally put the subdominant arm in a sling and has found significant differences in their speech.

56

8

VISION IN READING

The Berners reported in the following article certain success using the rationale outlined above by the author at a visual level only. The Berners considered the phenomena described as purely visual but the author feels that the visual factors are peripheral extensions of the basic neurological organization described in this work.

Reprinted from the *A.M.A. Archives of Ophthalmology,* November 1953, Vol. 50, pp. 603-608.

Relation of Ocular Dominance, Handedness, and the Controlling Eye in Binocular Vision.

George E. Berner, M.D. and Dorothy E. Berner, B.S. (Educ.) Philadelphia

Two papers published in 1938 marked the inception of this investigation. One,* by us, dealt with visual handicaps and reading difficulties. We mentioned that a relation between crossed dominance and reading disability seemed to exist but needed further investigation. The other,† by Walter Fink, summarized and presented for the special consideration of ophthalmologists the existing knowledge of ocular dominance and crossed dominance. He began his investigation convinced that the solution of any problems arising from crossed dominance lay in the field of psychological research; he reached the conclusion that the problem most probably could, and would, be solved by ophthalmologists, and he asked for continued diligent research in this field.

* Berner, G. E. and Berner, D. E.: Reading Difficulties in Children. *Arch. Ophth.,* 20:829-838 (Nov.) 1938.

† Fink, W. H.: The Dominant Eye: Its Clinical Significance. *Arch. Ophth., 19:*555-582 (April) 1938.

For those ophthalmologists to whom it is new, the problem is here briefly stated. Among the children of normal intelligence who meet difficulty in learning to read is a group with a characteristic pattern. It begins in early childhood with the slow development of motor co-ordination, often accompanied by speech hesitations or frank stammering. At school age the children show poor visual imagery and memory, and reversals in reading and writing patterns, sometimes including complete mirror writing. Very poor reading and spelling are the outstanding difficulties. Nervous fatigue accentuates the problem. In more mature life the combined appearance of ocular discomfort, nervous disorganization, and disruption of established reading habits suggests a similar pattern of later origin.‡

The connection of this chain of difficulties with crossed dominance has long been noted. For those to whom the problem is new, crossed dominance refers to the fact that the dominant (sighting) eye is on the side of the body opposite the preferred hand. But exhaustive surveys have failed to prove this a consistent link. Some children with crossed dominance have no such difficulties; some children with corresponding dominance exhibit the entire chain. The most complete survey is that of Johnston,¶ who found no correlation outside the operation of chance between anomalies of lateral dominance and reading disability in the group of children which he studied.

---

‡ Those who feel that a too comprehensive chain of symptoms has been suggested are referred to an article by J. Roswell Gallagher (Can't Spell, Can't Read.) *Atlantic, 181*:35-39 (June) 1948. The entire group of symptoms is there described by a physician-educator as part and parcel of a single problem.

¶ Johnston, P. W.: The Relation of Certain Anomalies of Vision and Lateral Dominance to Reading Disability. Monographs of the Society for Research in Child Development, Vol. 7, No. 2, Washington, D.C., National Research Council, 1942.

Fink § suggested, and we were then investigating, the probability that the source of this disability might lie in established patterns of binocular vision. Selzer§§ stated that he believed that "lack of integration resulting from lack of visual fusion will eventually prove to be the missing link of the situation." This assumption could easily be discarded, as these children proved to have good fusion and binocular stereoscopic vision.

When binocular vision has developed, there remains one visual act which is essentially monocular. This is the act of sighting.** The sighting eye is called the dominant eye. It is established in early life and is stable.

As binocular vision develops, it becomes habitual to use two eyes as a unit for visual perception. But within the pattern of binocular vision there is rivalry between the two eyes, and one eye controls binocular perception. This eye we have called "the controlling eye." The other eye plays an assisting, rather than an equal, role. The eye which controls binocular perception is not necessarily the eye with which the person sights. The sighting, or dominant, eye is selected for an essentially monocular act; the controlling eye gains its mastery within the pattern of binocular vision. The dominant eye is stable from early life, but the controlling eye can be shifted, as the binocular pattern is easily influenced by changes in vision, or controlled by training.

When a person has binocular vision, his motor reactions, speech, reading, and writing are initiated by binocular images. Our investigations have led us to believe that when the controlling eye is on the side opposite that of the handedness, the motor initiation is poor

§ Fink, W. H.: The Dominant Eye: Its Clinical Significance. *Arch. Ophth.*, 19:555-582 (April) 1938.

§§ Selzer, C. A.: Lateral Dominance and Visual Fusion: Their Application to Difficulties in Reading, Writing, Spelling, and Speech. Harvard Monographs in Education, No. 12, Cambridge, Mass., Harvard University Press, 1933.

** Walls, G. L.: Theory of Ocular Dominance. *A.M.A. Arch. Ophth.*, 45:387-415 (April) 1951.

and difficulties in speech, reading, and writing ensue. These difficulties can be relieved by shifting the control of the binocular pattern to the side of the handedness. Similar difficulties do not occur when the controlling eye is on the side of the handedness.

EXAMINATION, DIAGNOSIS, AND TREATMENT

The diagnosis of this condition and the direction of treatment are an ophthalmological problem. Educators cannot solve the difficulties encountered by the affected children without the aid of binocular vision examination, meticulous refractions, and supervision of the necessary occlusion or binocular vision training.

Children are referred to an ophthalmologist for consultation primarily for poor vision, for eyestrain caused by the use of eyes in learning, or for failure to learn, especially in reading and spelling, as well as others of their age and mental level. The examination of the last group should include questions on the development of muscular coordination, speech, and handedness. Notations of actual hand use should be made, including any attempted or accomplished change of handedness, and the occurrence of reversals in reading or writing ("saw" for "was," etc.) asked for.

The determination of ocular dominance by sighting tests is not necessary. It has been done in our series of cases for purposes of comparison, but it is unnecessary when a determination is made of the eye which controls the binocular vision. Examination of visual acuity, fundi, and muscle balance is routine. Examination of fusion, stereoscopic perception, and vergence powers follows. When the existence of binocular vision is accepted, we attempt to determine the controlling eye.

In the Keystone Visual Skills tests, published by the Keystone View Company and usable in a Telebinocular, are two cards, DB2-D and DB3-D. These cards compare the relative performance of the eyes during the act of binocular vision. It will often happen that an eye with relatively less visual acuity, as measured monocularly on a Snellen chart, performs noticeably better in picking out the dots on binocular targets, indicating that there is a strong demand for this eye to lead the binocular vision pattern. Great care must be exercised that these cards are exposed at infinity and that accommodative impulses of the eyes have been relaxed. We do this by presenting several interesting and easily fused stereoscopic pictures before the exposure of the targets. Percentages are read as given in tables on the back of these cards, and the function tested is noted as binocular efficiency.

Keystone Tests of Binocular Skill are used to determine the controlling eye in the binocular pattern of reading. These are selections at different reading levels of matched paragraphs for reading with two eyes together, the right eye alone with the left eye open, and the left eye alone with the right eye open. They are presented at the clearest reading distance. The reading is timed for number of seconds and errors. When a child cannot read at all, near-point vision is used for binocular fusion of such targets as Wells's E. Suppression and poor quality of a part of the fused image indicate the eye with relatively lower binocular efficiency.

A diagnosis of the controlling eye in binocular vision is made upon the data gathered in these examinations. The non-controlling eye may have relatively poor visual acuity with suspected refractive error. It may be a post-amblyopic eye that has never gained excellent use even though binocular vision has been established. It may have the same visual acuity as the controlling eye but lag when tested in the binocular pattern. The non-controlling eye may lag in the reading situation only; such children are less likely to give a history of preschool difficulty and have clearly defined difficulty with reading and spelling only. The diagnosis of hand-eye confusion is made when the eye which controls the binocular vision is on the side of the body opposite the hand used.

Treatment is directed toward measures which will establish the controlling eye in binocular vision on the side of the hand used. Refraction and the constant use of glasses may shift the binocular control. Occlusion, used as in the treatment of amblyopia, may be necessary, along with the use of glasses. Occlusion and limitation of all hand performance to one hand alone are the only treatment measures when refraction is normal. Treatment is continued until the controlling eye is established on the side of the handedness and remains in control after six weeks of unrestricted use of binocular vision.

SUMMARY AND CONCLUSIONS

During the course of studies of binocular vision, we met evidence which led us to form the following hypothesis:

(a) When the controlling eye in binocular vision is on the side of the handedness, no chain of symptoms referable to eye-hand confusion is likely to occur.

(b) When the controlling eye in binocular vision is on the side opposite the handedness, some part or all of the chain of symptoms is likely to occur.

(c) When two hands are used, the stronger the relative control of one eye (if the controlling eye is on the side opposite the more commonly used hand) the more likely symptoms are to occur. Reversely, if the use of a second hand disrupts a well-established eye-hand pattern on the opposite side, symptoms are likely to occur.

Investigation of more than 500 patients with and without symptoms of reading difficulty, defects of speech, and allied visual-motor disorganization convinced us that this hypothesis operates beyond the operation of chance.

Treatment based on these concepts is a distinct adjunct to the successful handling of many cases which reach the ophthalmologist in consultation.

This article clearly explains the procedures for evaluation, diagnosis and treatment at a visual level. The author feels that the Berners' rationale is by no means complete in that they have not related it to anything but the visual pattern. The author feels that the Berners' complete rationale fits into the rationale of neurological development; hence he feels that their procedures can be followed at a visual level but that procedures should, of course, be extended into the areas of audition, tonality, general physical control and dominance. He further feels that the evidence presented by the Berners' is corroborative evidence at a visual level towards a neurological rationale for resolving reading problems. The author feels that the Berners have made a very significant contribution to the field of reading and that their data should be incorporated as one aspect of the *total approach* to the solution of reading problems. As an example of the above rationale the author presents the following case history.

Boy D, age 12, righthanded, was referred to the author for remedial reading. When D's reading pattern was evaluated, it was found that the controlling eye in a binocular visual situation was the left eye, which was opposite his handedness. The left eye was also his sighting eye.

These areas were to be stressed in boy D's preremedial program:

1. His controlling and sighting eye (left) was to be occluded for two hours daily.
2. He was to be taught proper sleep patterns.
3. He was not to be allowed to use his left hand in other than a purely assistive way and he was not to be allowed to engage in any activity requiring sighting excepting on weekends.

On the weekend following the programming but prior to its actually being put in effect Boy D visited an amusement park. He spent some time shooting a .22 caliber rifle at moving targets. One of the shells exploded and severely damaged the left eye which was his dominant eye but on the side opposite his handedness. His eye became infected, and he was hospitalized.

Boy D permanently lost the sight of his left eye and because of the sympathetic reaction of his right eye was not able to read for the entire six week period that he spent in the hospital. He was retested one week after leaving the hospital on another form of the same test. The tests measured speed and accuracy of reading. His grade scores were 7.2 (94% accurate), before the accident, and 10.3 (94% accurate), after the accident and hospitalization. He showed a two-year improvement in grade level score in his oral reading. All other reading skills remained relatively static.

These improvements in speed and oral reading were made with no practice and very minimal use of the eyes. Because the sight of the left eye was permanently damaged at the time of the accident the second tests were taken monocularly. A follow-up of Boy D's reading two years later indicated that his reading patterns and mastery had accelerated significantly since the accident even though he had been unable to follow a planned remedial program. The author feels that the changed language pattern was directly related to the change in his visual status *and the neurological changes which accommodations to it entailed.* The author further feels that if the other two aspects of the pre-remedial program had been followed his spelling and comprehension would have made similar growths without the necessity of remedial teaching.

In evaluating vision as a part of the neurological whole, we have in addition to physiological appraisal of the eyes the following visual considerations.

We must first evaluate the sighting eye. This is easily done by having the individual sight by pointing with his index finger, and one can follow the sighting level back to the sighting eye. Another way of doing it is to hand the individual a monocular object such as a telescope and have him look through it. He usually chooses the sighting eye. Another way is to have the student assume a sighting stance, such as used in riflery, baseball, or any such activity. This preferred eye should be on the dominant side.

The next visual evaluation is that of the controlling eye. The best evaluative technique which the author has found thus far is the use of tests three, four and five of the Keystone Visual Survey Tests (Telebinocular). The controlling eye is the eye which comes out as the most efficient eye in a binocular visual situation as tested on tests three, four and five.

Following this we must ascertain the actual reading-visual function by checking the single eye which reads material best in a monocular situation. To ascertain this, one occludes one of the subject's eyes, has him read, times the reading and checks the errors. The same process is followed for the other eye. When the material read is of the same difficulty, the difference in results can be attributed only to the varying efficiency of the two eyes. The Telebinocular also has cards which test this efficiency in a binocular situation.

All three of these evaluative modalities result in pointing up the dominant eye. The sighting eye should fall on the dominant side; the controlling eye should fall on the dominant side; and the most efficient eye in reading, both in terms of time and errors, should fall on the dominant side.

In the event that they do not, we have an indication of a potential problem from a neurological-organizational point of view. In the event that the subdominant eye is the preferred or indicated eye in either a sighting, controlling or efficiency situation, it should be occluded so that the eye on the dominant side is made the more efficient eye. This occlusion should take place at first on a training-neurological level and secondly at the actual teaching level.

The author wishes to stress that the rationale presented by the Berners is biased toward a peripheral approach. The author feels that it is not the change-over of vision, it is not the change-over of one perceptive modality, that is responsible for the difference in performance, but that these peripheral activities help to change over the entire neurological structure; in other words, they help the organism to establish central dominance and by so doing tend to fit it into the entire scheme of neurological function. Vision as it applies to the neuropsychological approach to reading is a peripheral activity. Its effect under conditions described above is of a central nature.

As the author approached the neurological realm, it became immediately apparent that the neurological system must act as a whole. It quickly became apparent that if one were to deal with the problem of language, one had to deal with the whole person, not with an eye, hand, alphabet system of reading or type of teacher, but with the whole organism operating as a unit physiologically, psychologically and intellectually. Only through organizing the unit at its most efficient level, that of unilaterality, can a real solution to basic language deficiency arise.

9

EVALUATION AND TREATMENT PROCEDURES

Now let us use the theoretic concepts described above. First, we must take a very careful case history. The case history cannot be taken at one time because the parents must go home to observe the child for a week to be able to report on many of the items.

History: Date:

Name:
Address:
Chronological Age: Mental Age: I.Q._____

Grade: School:

Conditions at Birth:
    Labor (hours)   Forceps
    Anesthesia   Complications
    Color

Conditions at Birth of Other Siblings:

Handedness of Parents and Siblings:

Age of Walking:
Age of Talking: Words: Sentences:
Any speech deviation?

History of Illness — especially fractures — allergies — hospitalization and high temperatures.

History of Thumb sucking
    Which Thumb?

History of Development of Coordination

Fluid intake per day

Sleep Habits — to be observed by the parent and reported.
    Prone Position   On Back   *Other*

Singing ability — Enjoyment of music
    Describe

History of Hyper-Activity

Footedness	L____R____	
Handedness	L____R____	
Sighting Eye	L____R____	
Controlling Eye	L____R____	(Telebinocular)

Have child copy figures below:

Then proceed as follows:

Evaluate oral reading, look for stumbling over small words and for any signs of reversed reading. The reversed reading can be "was" for "saw," "on" for "no," down to letter reversals within words in both spelling and reading.

Evaluate spelling proficiency. Look for letter confusions such as spelling "very" for "every."

Evaluate reading by age and grade level. Use a test such as the Gates Reading Survey, which is analytic in nature, resulting in evaluations of vocabulary, speed and comprehension. (The cases described herein generally had much higher vocabulary scores than speed or comprehension scores).

Evaluate individual intelligence by using the Wechsler Intelligence Scale for Children, for group measurements use a test such as the California Test of Mental Maturity. These tests give both a verbal and non-verbal I.Q. (The cases described herein fall into the category of all remedial reading cases in that the poor reader generally scores much higher on the non-verbal section than on the verbal section.)

Compare the expectancy level with the reading level.

Ascertain hand preference and foot preference.

Ascertain sighting eye and controlling eye.

Set up the laterality configuration and the program for making the child completely unilateral.

The child is now put on a program of establishing neurological organization and laterality. First of all the child should be given every opportunity and every encouragement and guidance toward single handedness. He should not be allowed to use the subdominant hand excepting as an assistive hand. One of the difficult areas is sports. There are many times that even sports activities have to be changed so that the child becomes single handed. Any two handed sport for the time being should be discouraged, and any sport requiring binocular vision at a sighting level should also be discouraged. The child should be taught through physical conditioning to be single footed. He should be taught to lead off on the dominant foot; he should be taught to be generally physically one sided. In other words, if he should be right sided, he should be made right handed and right footed exclusively. No ambidexterity in either foot or hand should be allowed.

The ascertainment of the controlling eye or sighting eye should be validated. This can be done with the same Telebinocular as per above. In addition to this the child should read selections of equal difficulty monocularly to see if there is any significant difference in the reading performance of each eye. The subdominant eye should then be occluded for a period of one hour in the morning and one hour in the evening under proper medical supervision and the child should be encouraged to engage in sighting activity such as archery, riflery, etc., using only the dominant eye.

The child's fluid intake should be restricted gently as should be his intake of salts and sugars which tend to retain fluid in the body. Any habits such as thumb sucking, hair twisting, etc., should be done with the dominant hand, as the active hand (i.e., in thumb sucking, the left thumb to be sucked and the right hand to be used in exploratory activity if the subject is right handed.) As many monocular and one handed activities should be engaged in as possible using the hand, eye, foot of the dominant side.

All tonal activity should be ceased for the child. Music should be minimal, the child should not be allowed to sing and generally not allowed to listen to music for long periods of time. Records, radio and television programs should be of the story type.

Through physical conditioning the child should be taught adequate posturalization. The child through tonic-neck reflex activity should be given exercises in proper posturalization while awake and prone. The parents should posturalize the child upon his going to sleep and check the child hourly during early evening to see that the child is adequately posturalized. The child should also be so posturalized during any other rest periods. Such a program should continue for at least one month prior to the beginning of remedial reading activity.

The reading activity should originate at the word sight level. In other words, children at this point should begin to learn words at sight through configuration. Reading activity should be done in whispers by the subject. The subject should not tonalize any words but merely skill them through whispering. Oral reading should not be part of the program. The instruction should be relatively unstimulated and should be quiet, concise, precise and exacting. The author has found that teaching a child a sight vocabulary of one hundred and twenty-five words through this mechanism is a somewhat simple procedure. For those children who have learned some words and yet retained some of the difficulty, the work becomes quite simple and goes along quite rapidly at this point. Having established an approach to the reading, structural and phonetic analysis are introduced.

To recapitulate, we have now set up a mode of operations so that the human organism can become uniquely human in that it achieves unilaterality. In essence we have set up the organism from a sensory-motor point of view as a one-sided organism.

We have:

1. Made the dominant hand the skilled and most used hand. (*No ambidexterity.*)
2. Strengthened the dominant eye through occluding the subdominant eye.
3. Re-educated the child so that he has a dominant foot.
4. Deleted tonal activity (both sensory and expressive) so that the non-dominant cortical hemisphere assumes the most inactive role possible.

In addition to that we have set up the organism in sleep so that it operates on all of these premises. We have posturalized the organism so that it rests as a unit. The organism is aimed at unity both while active and at rest. All of this is prerequisite to remediation. After having set the neurological chain reaction in order, we tend to find that many of the original symptoms of reading retardation disappear, especially such symptoms as the confusion or reversal of letters within words in spelling and the reversal of words in reading and the reversal of words in speaking, and usually we find a complete disappearance of stammering and stuttering.

After a month to six weeks of such neurological organization we can begin with actual remedial training: If there remains a difficulty in establishing a sight vocabu-

71

lary, the author suggests a recapitulation of the diagnostic procedure so that any areas of judgment relative to the etiological factors be reconsidered. The author feels that technique alone is by no means an assurance of success, but if one orients the organism to neurological unity, technique then becomes an effective tool of remediation.

10

THE PREVENTION OF READING PROBLEMS

THE prevention of reading and language disabilities is probably the prime objective of this work. The author submits the following as examples of preventive measures.

A more natural birth process is to be desired. The obstetrical literature indicates that some forms of anaesthesia to the mother during birth tend to increase the possibility of anoxia because they decrease oxygenation for the child during the actual birth process. Children born naturally tend to have better coloring and breathe more spontaneously than those who are born with the mothers under certain types of anaesthesia. The literature has for some time stressed the necessity for proper prenatal supervision of diet. One of the important objectives of this supervision is to ease and speed the birth process. The obstetrical literature indicates an ever increasing awareness of the possibility of anoxia during parturition. New techniques for the elimination of the possibility of anoxia are being investigated constantly.

The concept of child care should be modified. Parents should be sensitized to the importance of anoxia and head injuries as potential language factors. Another important area of prevention in early childhood management is that of childhood crying. This is especially important from birth to eighteen months of age from a physical point of view. Crying does not always increase the cortical oxygen supply as is generally believed, there are times when crying decreases cortical oxygen supply. Although crying

73

and breath holding are rarely damaging to the organism in clinically observable areas, they are possibly functionally damaging to the most highly developed cortical cells (associational in function) which are the most vulnerable to trauma. These cells can be impaired organically with little or no observable physiological reaction; hence their impairment is impossible to observe excepting under associational (reading) conditions.

From a developmental point of view the author suggests the following preventive measures. From the age of nine weeks on children should be posturalized on their stomachs when put to bed. They should be posturalized with either hand prone. As there appears a subdominant hand it should become the prone hand with the thumb facing the child's mouth. As soon as a child develops a hand preference he should be encouraged to be single handed. Certainly we should not return to forcing children to a handedness. Children should not be encouraged toward a specific hand choice but should be encouraged toward consistency of hand choice. Because the psychological literature indicates that thumb sucking does satisfy certain needs, we should allow thumb sucking; *but we should not allow thumb sucking of the dominant hand. Thumb suckers should always suck the thumb of the subdominant hand.*

Ages five and six are critical ages in language development. Children at these ages should be taught games of skill wherein the sighting eye must be the dominant eye. If necessary to the reinforcement of the dominant eye, they should be taught such skills as shooting games, archery and ball games of the sighting type, so that they can become accustomed to sighting with the eye on the dominant side. Such experiences also reinforce hand-eye coordination.

During ages five and six tonal activity should be

74

kept at a minimum. Children should have a minimum of music and singing at this time in order to give them as much help as possible in establishing the skills which education requires of them during these years. Their music activities at pre-school and school should consist primarily of rhythmic activities. Group singing should become choral speaking with the emphasis on consonant skill and production instead of tonality. Children at this age should be taught listening, speaking and rhythmic skills with a minimum of tonal involvement.

Children should be encouraged to engage in unified one-sided activity. Too often parents and teachers allow confusing choices of sidedness even after a natural sidedness is evidenced. Too often parents allow children to have toys which discourage neurological unity. For example: Parents who buy toy guns for their children should buy either a rifle type gun or a single gun and holster to be worn on the dominant side. They should not allow children to have double holster gun sets which the children "draw" and "shoot" with both hands.

Mothers who are bottle feeding babies should shift the baby from arm to arm for alternate feedings. Babies' eating and sitting furniture and playpen position in the room should be changed periodically. When dressing young children always put the sock, shoe, mitten or glove on the dominant hand or foot first. When putting on underwear or trousers always put the dominant foot and leg in first, the same applies for shirts, sweaters, dresses and coats. Indeed watching a child dress is a very valid method for the evaluation of his unilaterality or lack thereof.

Until a child has indicated a true dominance tendency his crib should be placed with the headboard against a wall but with both sides away from a wall. When hand preference has been established the child's bedside may be placed against the wall but it should be so placed that when the child is in the bed prone his sub-dominant side is away from the wall.

Children should not be seated opposite each other for meals. Sitting opposite another person tends to increase mirroring or reversing on the part of children. Places at the table should be staggered so that imitation of a person sitting exactly opposite is not possible. Mirroring and imitation would increase the tendency to use the sub-dominant side of the body as the skill side. All eating utensils should be placed on the dominant side of the child's plate until the child has totally established dominance.

Children should always be handed articles on the preferred side. They should not be given obviously two-handed toys. Until they are unilateral they should be given one-handed toys or toys which are manufactured to require a skilled hand and an assistive hand for proper use. One must be especially careful in buying toys and games for left-handed children for most games and toys are marketed with right-handed children in mind.

Because of their bimanual nature swimming instruction and piano instruction should be postponed until unilaterality is established. Children should not be given phonograph records of music until handedness is established. Formal music lessons should never precede the establishment of dominance. Parents should explain and demonstrate new games and toys to children showing them proper hand and sighting choices before giving the toys to children. Children should not be allowed to have stereopticon type toys until after they are reading well. Children should be encouraged to use only the preferred hand with such early skills as crayoning, puzzle play and finger painting.

These suggestions are illustrative of the basic concept

76

relative to the establishment of dominance: *Until some preference for one side is evidenced naturally, both sides should be given equal opportunity to become dominant; when a choice appears naturally, every effort should be made to help the child to keep that side as exclusively unilateral as possible.*

Both teachers and parents must be made aware of the symptoms of neurological organization and the lack thereof so they can initiate preventive measures when a lack of neurological unity is evidenced. Such preventive measures must be begun by parents of very young children in the home, this should be continued by pre-school teachers, who should be sensitized to the clinical symptomology described herein.

The prevention of reading problems must continue in the first grade. Every effort of the teacher and the classroom organization should be aimed at reinforcing unilaterality and neurological unity. These efforts should even include such small details as posturalizing children properly during rest periods.

Children should be taught reading by wholes at the outset. To begin they should be given common experiences as a class group, such as going on a trip. Upon their return to the classroom, the teacher and children should discuss what they did and saw and the teacher should write an "experience chart" which is dictated by the children. The experience chart is made in sentence and story form. The children learn to read their own dictated sentences very easily. They also learn that reading is a meaningful process and that reading always progresses from left to right. After the sentences are recorded and read they are broken down into meaningful phrases. The children work at recognizing the phrases and the teacher again stresses the left to right progression in language. Having learned to recognize sentences and phrases containing between 100 to 150 words via this method, the children are given books which, through proper teacher planning, will contain most of the words met via the experience charts.

At this point tonality should be deleted from the program and reading recitations requiring skills should become whispered recitations. *Those children who have gone undetected but who lack neural unity manifest their symptoms at this stage,* mainly those of reversal tendencies. At this point a dualistic system of recognizing new words as wholes, recognizing them through small familiar words which make up the large words as well as through the sound components of words is effected. Critical at this point is the fact that *no child should be taught the letter-sound method until he has established complete unilaterality, has complete mastery of left to right progression (this usually takes more time and effort for left-handed children) and does not reverse letters or words. Continued reversal at this stage is an important indication to both teacher and parent that a program aimed at proper neurological organization should be instituted in order to preclude future reading retardation.*

Following this stage the teacher should make an evaluation of how each child masters language and reading skills most efficiently, and should teach the child via the method which best meets his needs. Teachers and parents must be cautioned that children vary and that no *"one"* method will be the most efficient for all children. At this point an ecclectic approach to method is ideal. The author wishes to restate that at this juncture in a child's mastery of the reading process *if neurological organization has been achieved, method is secondary.* This choice of method, therefore, is not related to outcomes but is instead related to the efficiency and ease with which each child can be helped to arrive at those outcomes.

When the child has established total neurological unity and when his reading and language functions are efficient and completely mastered he should be given complete autonomy in making laterality choices. Indeed, he must make changes in many of the restrictions above if he is to become efficient in managing his activities of daily living.

11

CASE HISTORIES

THE author wishes to caution the reader at this point. Many of the symptoms described herein tend to be, for the sake of description, the symptoms which stand out most clearly in remedial reading problems. The author has described the severe remedial reading problems. He feels, however, that those children who read well but who have such trouble as remembering proper spelling or displacing letters within words (which is not in keeping with their reading ability) can also be helped via this rationale.

The author further feels that a child with good reading can be helped to have even better language facility and better language aptitudes through the system of setting up a neurological organization which operates as a unity. *No doubt as man has evolved he has set up certain environmental blocks to his complete utilization of his neurological structure.* Hence if we can, through preventive activity or through educative activity, teach people neurological unity, we shall have done them a great service and shall perhaps make our good students even better, our good language people even better, our good spellers even better, our fluent speakers and listeners even better. Indeed we may be discussing a means for hurrying the evolutionary process. Let us take this example:

Boy X, born of mediocre parentage, with average intelligence; with siblings (two sisters, three brothers) all of whom were born with mediocre intelligence, suffered at the age of six months an accident which disabled his left arm. The child was never again, because of the injury, able to use his left arm. The arm hung at his side helplessly and its problem was of a purely peripheral nature, i.e., nerve severance at slightly below the shoulder level. Significantly this child, although there are many concomitant psychological variables, attended the same schools, was in the same activities as his siblings and yet rose to become one of the leaders in his profession and created many significant contributions to the world through the medium of language. Naturally this is only one case and cannot be used as evidence. However it does start one thinking toward the possibility of the utilization by man of his given neurological organizations to greater and greater advantage.

The author has used the rationale described herein on a number of teenage children who had on scholastic aptitude tests mathematical scores which were significantly higher than their language scores. He has found that after a period of four months of neurological organizational activities without any added teaching within the language realm, the language capacity indications on scholastic aptitude tests improved significantly.

These following case histories are listed in an effort to point up to the reader the implementation of the rationale described above.

Boy A, nine and a half years old when first seen by this examiner, presented a history of normal birth and early health, normal walking and talking onsets and generally normal development until the age of two. At this time the parents noticed aberrant behavior and some slight motor dysfunction. The parents, being very conscious of such things, immediately had the child evaluated and shortly thereafter the child underwent an operation for the removal of a large tumor in the *left* hemisphere of the cortex. Following the operation, recovery was smooth and without incident. The child relearned to walk, regained his speech very quickly, and went on as though there had been no former problem. The child's subsequent development was fine until he arrived at school. In the first and second grades he had great difficulty in school, not in terms of social activities but in terms of academic activities.

He was taken to a child guidance center which evaluated his intelligence on a Wechsler Intelligence Scale for Children at 126, with very slight deviation between performance and verbal levels. Many methods of teaching reading were used with this young man without success. He always had a pleasant personality, was always cooperative. The only deterrent to an otherwise ideal picture was a slight tendency toward hyperactivity. This hyperactivity was so slight that it was certainly not out of the normal range of expectancy. The boy's tonal ability was non-existent. He disliked music, never sang, and when asked to sing, sang in a monotone. He had had some training in singing because his parents wanted him to fit in to every aspect of his school life, but this training was most unsuccessful. His physical condition was excellent, his general coordination was fair, and he generally was a healthy young man. His vision was normal, he did not wear glasses. The only problem in the visual pattern was that the sighting eye and controlling eye were on the right side, in conflict with his handedness, which was generally left, with only slight ambidexterity, and his footedness, which was always left.

His sleep pattern was disorganized, he slept in a prone position, face down, in a spread-eagle pattern. We have a picture of a left handed boy with slight manual ambidexterity, a totally right footed boy, a right eyed boy, a non-tonal boy. There were no other neurological signs or residuals of the operation. His reading level was typical of children such as this, his reading was saturated with reversals, not only of letters within words but of full words. His spelling was very poor. He was unable to spell the simplest words, having been unable to learn phonetic or structural word analysis. His arithmetic computation was quite good; the only real deterrent to his even better achievement was the fact that he reversed numbers in much of his computation. Although this boy had received three years of schooling combined with three years of tutoring, he was unable to read. His reading level was at the first grade or pre-primer level. His parents had taken him from one reading clinic to another and from one remedial teacher to another. He had been given one full year of daily Fernald treatment (for one hour per day) with no apparent success. He had been given a full educational approach to phonetics and structural analysis with no apparent success.

The parents were deeply distressed by his problem. Having felt after the operation that they were very lucky in having a very normal child, they now began to feel that they had a child who lacked one basic factor in intelligence which would mar his entire life. He was diagnosed at other reading clinics as an associative learning problem who needed a good deal of analytic approach to reading and also a good deal of the Fernald VAKT technique. There was no question as to Boy A's personality as an etiological factor because he was an always happy, outgoing, fun-loving child. His parents were deeply concerned with his needs and were approaching his problems in a very logical although somewhat over-emotionalized fashion.

Boy A was put under the following pre-remedial program. His left footedness was reinforced by giving him activities which required kicking. He spent much time merely kicking a ball. His handedness was made totally unilateral on the left. He was not allowed under any circumstances to use his right hand for single handed activity and was constantly educated toward using his left hand as the leading hand in bimanual activities and as the only hand in singular handed activities. He was taught new proficiencies in throwing with the left hand. He was taken out of all sports other than those aimed at further establishing handedness and footedness and those which required sighting, such as basketball and baseball. His right eye (subdominant eye) was occluded every other hour for a period of an hour. During that time he used his left eye and saw only monocularly.

His sleeping position was changed to a posturalized position wherein he slept with the right arm flexed, his face facing his right thumb, his right knee flexed, and his left leg and left arm extended. He was not allowed to attend music classes at school and was not allowed to listen to music at home during the six week pre-remedial period. It was reported by his teachers during the latter part of the six week pre-remedial period that Boy A seemed to be making infinitely more progress without tutoring.

Having established neurological unity and unilaterality at the end of the six week period, a remedial program was instituted. The results were dramatic. Boy A practically read spontaneously. At the end of a month it was decided that he no longer needed the phonetic and structural analysis which were being given to him in a remedial situation for he read at a beginning third grade level. At this juncture his teacher, in conference, indicated to both the parents and to the author that she felt sure that the child could continue his accelerated reading growth and that no further remedial activity was necessary. At her suggestion there was no further remedial activity other than the continuation of the program outlined above. When the author saw this child six months later, he was reading up to his grade level; and the hope of his teacher was to get him slightly above that level because his IQ so indicated.

The author feels that these results were made possible by changing the undamaged subdominant hemisphere into the dominant hemisphere and by giving unity to the neural structure that resulted.

Girl B, age eleven. Girl B was brought to the author because of her inability to learn to read at the level at which she was expected to read. Girl B was in many ways a musical genius. She had studied the piano since the age of four, had given concerts, and was well known in the musical field. Her piano playing was extraordinary. She had two strong hands. Her musical aptitude was rated as being that of relative pitch, that is, if one played a note or sang a note for her at random, she could tell what the note was. She was a very highly skilled musician, was good in arithmetic, but did very poorly in all areas of language. Her early history was normal, the onset of walking and talking fell within the normal range. Her IQ was 125 with a verbal IQ of 140 and a non-verbal IQ of 120. Her personality studies indicated an adequate personality structure with good adjustments. She was a quiet girl who tended to be happy when alone or with a very few friends. She did not socialize with a large group of friends.

Her parents were deeply concerned because her musical activities, her social interactions and her general maturity far outstripped her abilities to read and to write. She had received a good deal of phonetic training and had received a good deal of remedial reading teaching, but her reading continued to be of a third grade level. Her spelling was very poor, and her handwriting was only fair. There were no gross neurological indications of dysfunction, and her physical condition was excellent. Evaluation indicated a fantastically developed tonal ability and tonal memory system, which was no doubt a part of her musical training. She was right handed, right footed and tended to be right eyed; there was only a slight tendency toward left eyedness, but, for other than a few situations wherein she was frustrated or tired, she was right eyed. Her sleep pattern was good; she slept in the proper position. There was no indication of a traumatic etiology in her problem.

Although she had defied diagnosis other than pointing up her need to work harder on her reading in prior evaluations, it was the feeling of the author that treatment should be followed in terms of the rationale outlined above. The handedness problem probably had been contributed to in part by a too early training of an ambidextrous nature (piano playing). Coupled with this the tonal factors (subdominant) were trained to such a degree that cortical unilaterality of a dominant-subdominant relationship was impossible.

The author therefore recommended the following program. The child was not allowed, for a period of six weeks, to engage in any ambidextrous activity; hence her piano playing ceased for a period of six weeks. At the same time tonal activities, which are in the subdominant area (and are therefore apt to increase the tendency toward a lack of unilaterality) were also taken out of her schedule. She was not allowed to play the piano. She could do her piano exercises *with her right hand only* on a measured silent piano board, not at the piano. She was not allowed to hear music or to sing for the period of six weeks. No other activity was recommended for her.

At the end of the six week pre-remedial period a further evaluation was made. Evaluation indicated at this time that her piano playing by the left hand had deteriorated significantly. Her right hand at this point seemed much better than her left because of the difference in practice. Her relative pitch deteriorated to a degree in that she now could be fooled many times as to which note she heard. A check of her controlling and sighting eye indicated that the right eye had become reinforced during this six week period and that she now used the right eye exclusively.

There followed a two month period of remedial reading in one hour sessions five days per week. At the end of the two month period she had mastered the concepts of phonetic and structural analysis and could use them in word attack and word analysis. Her vocabulary scores had increased very significantly, her speed of reading was much improved, and her general reading level placed her at her expectancy level. Her school marks improved significantly and she became a very happy and very successful student.

The author must mention, however, that her parents were only mildly happy about the overall improvement because her musical abilities which formerly approached genius level, had now deteriorated to the point of her being an only superior musician. The parents considered her learning to read a mixed blessing for as she learned to read, her musical competency, her tonal memory and her left handed music playing had all deteriorated to the point that she no longer held the great promise of a musical career which she had held formerly.

Boy C, a six year old blind boy. This boy was a premature baby, he had no physical problem other than his sight. He was brought to the author because of a very severe stuttering problem. The problem was so severe that Braille reading readiness activity could not be begun because of this great speech problem. The boy's developmental history, after his early problems of being premature, was fairly normal. Although his IQ could not be measured, his general behavior, when one considered his visual limitations, certainly indicated that he had adequate intelligence.

His general physical condition was good; he tended to be hyperactive, waving his arms around and slapping his sides, only when he became very frustrated. His sleep pattern was disorganized; indeed there was no pattern. He had excellent tonal memory and ability. He could hear a song once and could sing it, repeat it; and his memory for words was very good when there was music attached. His stuttering always disappeared when he was singing. This was no doubt the result of the fact that when he was singing the tonal area was carrying the skill area, hence there was no conflict and no stuttering. When one deleted the tonal area and had him say the same words, he could not say them without stuttering. As there was obviously no reading pattern, the main problem which brought the boy to the author was his poor speech. The boy was decidedly right footed but he was very ambidextrous. He had had speech stimulation and speech therapy with no apparent effect.

The following program was set up. He was first of all posturalized in his sleep, and he was taught that this was the way he was to position whenever he was resting. He slept prone with his face toward his left hand, which was prone and flexed, and his left leg was flexed, his right foot and his right arm were extended. He was put on a program of fluid restriction and was not allowed more than thirty ounces of fluid per day. He was not allowed to sing or to listen to music. All musical activities were deleted from his environment.

Because of the great difficulty in keeping him right handed, it was decided to put his left arm in a sling (in essence immobilizing it) for alternate hour periods during the day, that is, one hour of immobilization and one hour of freedom. When the parents heard the recommendations, they accepted them completely but indicated that they felt that their son would not accept them. In fact, they indicated that he would probably rebel against the whole program. Nevertheless, his pre-remedial period was evaluated as fairly successful.

Boy C did sometimes cheat on the amount of fluid and when frustrated did sometimes pull his hand out of the sling to use it ambidextrously. However, the overall picture of his acceptance of the program was fair. He did not receive any remedial teaching or speech therapy because by the end of the fifth week his stuttering had disappeared so completely that the parents felt that his problem had been entirely solved, and the teachers put him into their kindergarten reading readiness program. The teacher's last report to the author indicates that the boy's speech is now normal and his reading is improving.

Boy D. This young man, age eighteen years, was brought to the attention of the author because a college admissions committee had pointed up the fact to his parents that his scholastic aptitude evaluations indicated an arithmetic aptitude and mastery at the ninetieth percentile of college applicants and a language aptitude and mastery at the thirtieth percentile of college applicants. The young man was well rounded in terms of extracurricular activities. He was a fine musician, playing the trumpet, and was an excellent athlete.

His prowess in football and basketball was what brought him to the attention of the college. He was not only a good backfield runner in football; he could pass the ball with either hand, running in either direction in basketball and football.

Evaluation indicated that he had earned fair marks during his elementary and prep schooling but that he had struggled through school, taking a great deal of time with all the areas of education involving language; and conversely he had done extremely well, yet taking very little time, in all the areas involving mathematics. His birth, early health and developmental history were normal, his walking and talking onsets were quite normal. His IQ, as measured by a Wechsler, was 142 with a verbal of 115 and a performance of 160. He was a very friendly young man, outgoing, sure of himself, and very concerned about getting into college. He had had many scholarship offers but had chosen this particular college because his father had gone there. Boy D knew that the language requirements for this college were beyond his present competencies.

Evaluation indicated that his tonal ability was excellent. He had good tonal memory and had excellent musical ability. He played the trumpet quite well and yet had studied and practiced very little. His physical condition was excellent, and his activity level was within normal range. An evaluation of his handedness indicated that he was for all small muscle skilled activities, left handed. He was ambidextrous only in gross activities, such as throwing, playing tennis, and golf, in which he had cultivated a facility with his right hand. He was definitely left eyed both in terms of visual control and in terms of sighting. His sleep pattern was well organized but was *negative*. In other words, he slept with his face toward his left hand, which was flexed, and his left knee was flexed, with his right arm and right leg extended.

Following the diagnosis both the parents and the boy decided that they would wait to see what they would do. The college rejected the boy's application. He not only lost out on the application, but he also lost a scholarship which would have been awarded to him had he been accepted.

Following this very serious upset the boy was brought back to the author, and the following program was instituted. The boy was put into a school for a post-graduate year. Because he made the scholastic and athletic age limit he was to be allowed to play football that fall. The first change in his program was the fact that he no longer was allowed to throw with his right hand, to play golf or tennis, or engage with his right hand in any activity which is normally done on one side of the body by unilateral human beings. He had to throw all footballs and play all games using his left hand. He was also made left-halfback on the ball team. Whenever he moved on the football field, his left foot stepped out first. All gross muscle activities, therefore, were done with the left hand. There was no change in the small muscle activities, such as writing, simply because he already did all of those things with his left hand.

The trumpet playing was deleted from his program for two reasons. First of all, he played the trumpet holding it in his left hand and pushing down the keys (which requires skill) with his right hand. This was in opposition to the laterality pattern which we were trying to establish. In addition to that fact we wanted to discourage the stimulation of the sub-dominant hemisphere insofar as possible. Nothing was done with him in the field of vision, because he was left eyed, excepting that all games of a sighting nature which he was playing, such as tennis, had to be done with the left hand. This again reinforced the visual pattern with the left eye as the sighting and controlling eye.

There was a great difficulty in helping him to change his sleep pattern of posturalization. However, he did accede to having his father changing him around while he was asleep whenever it was noticed that he was not sleeping in the proper position. We changed him to facing the opposite side, that is, with his right hand prone, his face facing his right hand, his right leg flexed, and his right arm flexed, his left leg and arm extended.

He was not allowed to listen to music and, as per above, was not allowed to make music. We also insisted that during the pre-remedial period he read for one and one-half hours per evening using an occluder over his right eye and whispering all of the words which he read. There was no tonality involved, he was merely to use the mouth-lip skills.

Following the six week pre-remedial period a tutoring situation was set up for him of three hours per week. The tutoring was aimed at improving his facility with vocabulary and English in general. Reading at this stage was allowed to be secondary. After four months of such tutoring he took the scholastic aptitude tests and scored an eighty-fifth percentile on the language area. Naturally, there was some consideration of added age in this situation, but this was a far more significant gain than is typical in just the passage of time. The boy was accepted the following year by his college, did well in the academic realm, but did only fairly well in the realm of athletics.

———

Doctor H, age sixty-two years. Dr. H, a prominent

preacher who was well known in his city as a radio evangelist, was the victim of a cerebral vascular accident. In order to save his life he was operated on because of continuing hemorrhaging, and, as a consequence, much of his dominant cortical hemisphere was removed. As a result Dr. H was a right sided hemiplegia who could not speak, read, walk or use his right arm. He also suffered a visual hemianopsia. Dr. H spent seven years trying to become rehabilitated. He made excellent progress physically, learned to walk again, talk again, use his hand (primarily as an assistive hand), but he could not relearn to read. Dr. H had always enjoyed music and had excellent singing ability which no doubt was in part responsible for his spiritual successes. Because reading was paramount to Dr. H professionally, he did not consider himself rehabilitated until such time as he was able to read his sermons over the air. Dr. H spent many years and thousands of dollars seeking reading instruction. He was subjected to all of the present modalities of instruction with no success. The decision was then made to have Dr. H taught to read from a neuro-psychological point of view.

Because the operative notes indicated that the dominant hemisphere of the cortex had been in great part removed, the decision was made to change his laterality to the other side completely. The following program was set up:

Dr. H was sent to a physical therapy program wherein he worked the entire day with exercises to establish him as a left handed person. He worked in occupational therapy to gain skills in his left hand. He was made left footed. The entire program was aimed at giving him skills on the left side of his body and to make what was the subdominant cortical hemisphere the dominant hemisphere. Concurrently with this program Dr. H's right eye was occluded, again in order to make his left eye the sighting or controlling eye in a binocular visual situation. Dr. H was not allowed to hear music or to sing music. This was done in order to cut down the tonal function of the subdominant area and thereby to focalize it as the skill area. This part of the program went on for six weeks.

The entire program was aimed at setting up a new neurological framework. We were in essence making Dr. H one sided but changing the side. This was done so that the hemisphere which was intact would become the skill hemisphere and through this hemisphere we would be able to teach Dr. H to read.

After six weeks of the above Dr. H was taught the fundamentals of reading. He was taught the word sight method in conjunction with phonetic and structural analysis (finding small words in large words). His successes during the first weeks of the program were significantly greater than he had achieved in all the years he had received other types of instruction. The success was not due to superior teaching but was the result of the neurological organization and reorientation that took place prior to the teaching.

———

Boy E, age twelve years. Boy E was brought to the author because, as his parents described it, he was word blind. Although twelve years old, he could not read beyond a second grade level. He was a pleasant young man in appearance, slow moving, and certainly got along well with his peers. He got along well at home and seemed to have no real problem other than his inability to deal with language. He had been educated in both public and private schools and had been to two reading clinics, one of which diagnosed him as an associative learning disability and recommended a visual, auditory, kinesthetic and tactile approach to reading. This was followed daily for one year and was completely unsuccessful. The second reading clinic to which the young man went diagnosed his problem as an emotional problem. It was the feeling at this clinic that the boy although giving every impression of trying to do well was really punishing his parents and the world by not doing well. Therefore his reading disability was the result of an unconscious wish not to read. There followed a two year psychotherapy which did not result in any improvement in his reading.

The case history indicated a very long labor but with no apparent birth trauma. The onset of walking and talking were somewhat late but not extraordinarily so. The IQ of Boy E as measured by the Wechsler Intelligence Scale for Children was 120 with 125 verbal IQ and 115 performance IQ. There certainly was no question at this stage as to his personality for he had been psychoanalyzed and released by the psychoanalyst as a very adequate personality.

His physical condition was excellent. He did, however, have somewhat poor gross muscular coordination, and his fine muscle coordination was quite poor as indicated by his very poor handwriting and his very poor manual dexterity with either hand. In checking dominance we found that he was definitely right footed, definitely right handed but mildly left eyed. There was no indication of ambidexterity in either the foot or the hand but it was noted that there was some lack of coordination in all ends, which included his right leg and right foot and right hand. He had no sleep pattern; he slept in many ways: spread eagle, false pattern, and on his back. He verged on being a monotone. He did not particularly enjoy music, nor could he produce music very well. He had never studied music. He never learned nursery rhymes as a little boy partially because of the disinterest of his mother and partially because he had such great difficulty in singing them.

His reading patterns were pathetic. Although he had had two years of reading of a remedial nature, one of the VAKT method and one of the phonetic method, and superimposed upon that had had a two year psycho-analysis, his reading frustration level was at the second grade level. He could not read first grade materials comfortably. He miscalled words, had no real approach to analyzing words and found it very difficult to sit down to be instructed in reading because of the frustrations involved. His spelling was non-existent. He had no concept as to phonetics, word analysis or how to go about finding component parts of words. Truly in terms of functional reading and spelling he was word blind.

Because of the severity of the problem and the great difficulty of diagnosis it was decided to try a full program on Boy E to see whether we could make some difference in his reading pattern. His parents who were wealthy had had him tested and retested and tutored and taught reading in so many ways and so many places that we had to break down a natural resistance to failure in all reading activities. When the program of pre-remedial activity was outlined to Boy E he accepted it, primarily on the basis that it did not include any reading activity. In order to gain his full cooperation we asked his school (he was at that point attending a remedial school) to discontinue all phases of language and language development and reading during the six week pre-remedial session.

Boy E was first taught to use his right foot and his right hand in a more skilled fashion. He was taught the rudiments of athletics, in which he did not do well, so that he could gain greater skill in these activities. He was taught to make small articles, such as models, using his right hand so that he could gain as much skill as possible with both the right hand and the right foot both in fine muscle activity and in gross muscle activity.

There followed a period of occluding his left eye. The ophthalmological examination of his vision indicated that in a controlling binocular visual situation his left eye was the more efficient eye. Therefore the left eye was occluded daily for alternate hours and was checked at two week intervals. At this point it was found that there was no significant difference in the visual pattern. The occlusion was made more consistent. His left eye was occluded for an hour and forty-five minutes, and then he was allowed a fifteen minute binocular period. Following that there was another hour and forty-five minutes of occlusion, followed by a fifteen minute unoccluded period.

He was posturalized in sleep and was taught how to posturalize at any time during which he rested. There was some difficulty in getting him to accept this, but with the cooperation of his parents he was consistently sleeping in the correct position of lying face down with his face facing his left hand and arm which were flexed and his left leg flexed with the right arm and right leg extended by the third week. All music was deleted from his program, and he was not allowed to hear music nor to sing music. He was not allowed to read aloud. He was put on a program of fluid restriction. There was no true basis for suspecting a traumatic etiology, but in order to be safe it was decided to rule this out by trying the fluid restriction program.

At the end of the six week pre-remedial period a further evaluation was made, and it was found that unilaterality both of a central and a peripheral nature was being established. However, it was decided to continue the program for another four weeks so that a complete

97

neurological unity and neurological organization could be accomplished.

Following this ten week pre-remedial session it was decided to begin remedial reading activity. All reading activity was tuned at the word sight method. There was no phonetic involvement at the outset nor was there any tracing. The program began with experience charts from a word-sight point of view and progressed as it would progress in a normal classroom, the only change being that there was never a spoken word. Everything was whispered, not only were the experience charts which were read whispered and the discussions whispered, but when Boy E read he always read in a whisper. The teacher talked to him and read with him in whispers.

This activity went on for two hours per day five days per week for the period of one month, at which time the first evaluation of his reading was made. By the end of this first month he read at 3.5 grade level having improved one and one-half years in reading. By the end of the second month he read at a 5.5 grade level, having accomplished in the second month an additional two year grade level improvement. As he read at the 5.5 grade level and because of his great former problem of schooling and remedial work, it was decided at this point to put him back in a normal school situation, and he has done well ever since. Many times, as with this case, it is difficult to diagnose the exact area in which the change has to be made, but with this type of case and with the severity involved the author feels that a total approach using all techniques at our command is sometimes indicated.

Case study six. This case study includes thirty children. These children were taken from a number of schools, and the criteria for choosing them were as follows: Each child had to be in the lower third of his class and each child had to be at least one and one-half years retarded in reading, that is, he had to read at least one and one-half years below his expectancy level. Each child was checked for visual control in a binocular situation and for sighting and either the controlling eye or the sighting eye was on the subdominant side. These children were in the third, fourth and fifth grades. They were both boys and girls.

Using the criteria of the one and one-half years retardation and the controlling or sighting eye on the subdominant side, it was decided to put the following program in effect with these children without any further diagnostic procedures. These children first all had the subdominant eye occluded for one hour each morning and one hour each evening at home. Each child received two lecture-demonstrations on posturalization in sleep. They were shown how to sleep and had the reasons for posturalization explained to them. Tonal factors were deleted as much as possible from each child's program. Naturally with such a large group and in various homes and schools the program could not be followed completely. Their musical activities were kept minimal, their radio listening and their singing were kept minimal. These children were also required to whisper all of their reading, not to read it aloud.

Based on the program, which was followed with fair to good consistency for a period of eight weeks, the children's reading was then evaluated objectively by tests. It was found that the reading growth during the eight week period was as follows: The maximum reading growth was 2.3 years. The median reading growth was nine months. The minimum reading growth was four months. With no other diagnostic procedures involved the author feels that the approach used above and the results thereof certainly indicate that the rationale contained herein is quite applicable to the normal classroom activity for children who present slight deviations in reading as well as for children who present gross reading retardation.

As we look at the study above we must conclude that since various teachers used the method, their teaching systems were not changed, and since various schools, various families, various communities cooperated in the program the new growth certainly could not have been the result of any changes in routine or changes in technique but were instead the result of changes in the neuro-organization of the children. The remainder of each class was checked (those children who did not follow the program outlined above), and their growth fell into the normal growth pattern, that is, the median growth was two months, the maximum growth was five months, and the minimum growth was one month. We must conclude that the program outlined for the poor readers was certainly responsible for a very great difference in their reading growth.

———

Boy F, age ten, was brought to the author because all testing indications were that this boy was very bright but he could not read. The aggregate testing program indicated an IQ between 150 and 170. The schooling which this boy had received was both progressive and conservative but in general was very good schooling. He had received the finest of remedial techniques, his parents had spent a great deal of time and money on him, with no apparent improvement in his reading picture. Prior to our seeing him he had received six months of psychotherapy with no apparent improvement in his reading.

Birth conditions were fairly normal excepting that forceps were used and labor was longer than typical. There were no marks or injuries. There was a normal walking, talking onset and the boy, when seen by the author, seemed a perfectly healthy, active and extremely bright young man. Personality studies were not made by the author because he had received from the psychotherapist a complete appraisal of the boy and an indication that the boy was a well-adjusted personality. Boy F had excellent tonal ability, he could carry a tune and had excellent tonal memory. His voice was of excellent quality, and he sang in the local church choir. The patterns of handedness and footedness were right sided for the foot and left sided for the hand. Upon checking the controlling and sighting eye it was found that the sighting eye and controlling eye were on the right side.

We had therefore a human being who had a right sided dominant eye and foot but who used his left hand. He slept in a cross pattern, that is, with his left hand flexed and his left leg extended and the right leg flexed. He slept in this confused pattern consistently. His reading patterns were woefully inadequate although he had received much remedial reading work: his phonetic analysis was very weak; his word attack was very poor; he tended to reverse letters, words; and generally he disliked both the process and the idea of reading.

The following program was set up for him. First of all, all left handed or ambidextrous activities were discouraged. He was made right handed. We ran into some difficulty with this in that he had a tendency to want to use the left hand because of precedent. In order to help him to become a fully right handed human being we taught him throwing and tennis, and during the pre-remedial period we gave him writing exercises with his right hand. That is, we taught him to use his right hand in the most highly skilled manner possible. We did not have to do anything further to change his handedness. We deleted all tonality and we deleted all reading for the time being. He was not allowed to sing or to listen to music and we felt that he should not receive remedial instruction while going through the pre-remedial activity.

He took the program very seriously and really worked at it. We ran into a complication at the end of the six week period as a result of deciding to continue the pre-remedial period for another four weeks. His parents, unknown to the author, decided that he had made such strides that they began having him tutored for a two hour period per day during the fifth, sixth, seventh, eighth, ninth, and tenth weeks of the pre-remedial program. During the seventh week we noticed that there was some beginning hesitation in the speech of the young man.

At this particular point a reevaluation was made and we found that the reversal tendency had decreased in his reading, and that his spelling was improved. However, we were very concerned with the development of a stammer in his speech. In checking it and going over it with the parents we found that he was being given remedial activity during this program. The parents saw the lack of wisdom of their action and ceased. The remedial activity, however, was not discovered until the tenth week of the pre-remedial period. It was decided, therefore, to continue the pre-remedial program for weeks eleven, twelve, thirteen and fourteen. We continued the pre-remedial program without any other interference, without any reading teaching, and at the end of the fourteenth week it was found that all of the areas with which we were concerned had become unilateral and the stammer had disappeared. We were now ready to give him remedial work.

The remedial work consisted of practically a spontaneous learning to read. Within three weeks the remedial work was stopped because the young man had learned to read to the point at which he could compete with his classmates, and he did very well in the normal classroom situation thereafter. No further remedial work was required by the school. He has been in school for a number of years and is now an honor student.

Boy G. Boy G was brought to the clinic to be seen by the author because he was having great difficulty with beginning reading. He had no real concept of words, of word analysis, and had great difficulty from the very first day of the first grade year. He was born in a breach position and was bluish at birth. The developmental case history indicated that he was quite slow in developing speech, words, and sentences and quite slow in developing walking. IQ indications were of an IQ of between 90 and 95. Reading readiness scores placed him at the fortieth percentile of the six year old group at the beginning of first grade. The parents were very apprehensive as to his future success, both in the first grade and in school. The developmental history indicated somewhat slow early childhood development. Although the boy was perfectly healthy when seen by the author, the onset of talking was slow, the onset of walking was also slow. Tonal ability was very poor. The child did not particularly appreciate music, could not carry a tune very well, and was not interested in music.

Seeing a child at the age of six raises certain difficulties in terms of both central dominance and peripheral dominance. One can not assume that manual dominance has

103

been established nor can one assume that visual dominance in terms of sighting eye and controlling eye have been established. In evaluating the reading level one could find only initial frustration with the entire reading process. There was a tendency to reverse patterns, letters, pictures, otherwise there was no real reading pattern. Gross coordination was fair to poor. The general coordinational picture seemed to be one fitting at the bottom of the normal range scale. The electroencephelogram studies indicated a picture which fell within normal limits.

It was decided to have the child continue in the first grade with remedial help of a supportive nature until such time as a dominance pattern would evolve. Upon re-evaluation six months later it was found that there was no dominance pattern, the child was approaching the age of seven, and there seemed to be no indication that he would set such a pattern. It was decided at that point to put the child in a program which would help him to establish such a pattern, assuming the need for neurological organization and assuming in part a potential anoxic etiological factor was involved.

Boy G was first put on a fluid restriction program which allowed him to have thirty to forty ounces of fluid intake per day. A program of initiating handedness and footedness was established. He was given consistently a number of choices of a singular sidedness to make in terms of feet and in terms of hands. As we approached the second week, it was found that his best hand seemed to be his right hand. It was, in terms of a great number of choices, the hand which was used most. A visual evaluation indicated that both eyes functioned normally.

It was decided in light of these facts to have him become a right handed human being. It was also noted that in the family history there was no left handedness or ambidexterity. Therefore the left eye was occluded for one hour to every three hours of unoccluded vision. He was posturalized in sleep as right handed. All tonal factors which emanate from the subdominant hemisphere were eliminated so that the dominant hemisphere could become truly dominant. All reading activities were done in a whisper, and insofar as was possible every time the child was taught any reading in a remedial situation it was done in a whisper.

This child, his parents and his teachers followed the program conscientiously. They have been following this program for the past three years. No longer is it necessary to train the handedness and footedness. The vision has come to the point that he is now right eyed in a binocular visual situation. His sleep posturalization is natural. He does not involve himself with tonal activities because of a lack of experience therein and also because he has no real accomplishments in this area. He has learned to read without having had to repeat the first grade. He has gone on through school and he is now reading with his class group and has developed with his class group to a point wherein he exceeds the class median in reading by six months.

He is now in the fourth grade and doing quite well. He continues to lag behind in athletic skills and motor functions. His writing continues to be poor but is much improved. His spelling has improved by leaps and bounds, and he remains now only one year behind the median for his group in this area. The prognosis for his future success in terms of his original problem and in terms of his relatively minimal potential intelligence seems to be very good.

———

Boy H, an adopted English war orphan, had a very severe visual aphasia and a very severe problem of association coupled with many other factors. When the author first saw him he was nine. His reading was non-existent although he had had two years of excellent schooling and one year of very concentrated remedial reading. At the age of nine he could not tell the difference between a b and a d. He reversed not only in reading and writing, he also reversed periodically in speech. At the age of nine he had not established any sidedness. Because his birth records had been destroyed during World War II, we had no developmental history.

This boy presented an almost classical clinical picture of neurological disorganization, and yet the studies made on the electroencephalogram indicated that he fell within normal limits. The problem arose as to how to treat such a boy. There was no indication as to any sidedness; there was no indication as to any visual sidedness, foot sidedness or hand sidedness. The final judgment relative to sidedness was made through his sleep patterns. In sleep he periodically chose a right handed pattern in which to sleep and seemed to be more comfortable in that pattern than any other position. It was decided to make him a right handed human being and a right sided human being.

The entire program was instituted for him. He was made completely right handed. His left hand was immobilized (put in a sling) early in the pre-remedial period for a short time. He was taught games which required single footedness and handedness, and it was insisted that he become right handed and right footed. His left eye was occluded so that he had to use only the right eye during alternate periods of one hour of occlusion and one hour of binocular vision. He was posturalized in sleep consistently and all tonal factors were taken out of his environment. All reading activities were done with him in whispers.

106

At the end of the six week pre-remedial period it was found that the progress made toward unilaterality and central dominance was minimal. It was decided to continue the program for another six week period. At the end of that period we saw some improvement but not enough to warrant its discontinuation. We instituted another six week period.

At the end of the eighteenth week of the program we felt that we had made certain inroads toward neurological unity and central dominance. However, we continued to have great difficulty in teaching him any semblance of clarity of perception in reading or association. We decided to begin with visual-auditory reading at this point, using only his right side. We found that we made some inroads on his reading problem but that we had by no means solved the problem. Boy H and his mother conscientiously followed everything we suggested for a period of six months, with what they considered very dramatic success but with what we considered minimal success.

At this stage we decided to add to the program a restriction of fluid, and to add to the program a new approach to the reading, that of the word-sight method and phonetic analysis. We began to see real signs of improvement at this point, and during the following summer months he showed what were to be his most dramatic gains. During one six week period he gained two and one-half years in reading, and we found that as the reading rate accelerated he improved also, both as a human being and as a student in his school.

He now remains about one year retarded in reading and is continuing the program in full, including the fluid restriction. We feel that this boy was one of our most difficult cases in terms of language problem and neurological unity. We feel that the continuation of the program, if he is to be totally successful within the framework of his capacities, will be a very long term process at least until such time as he can operate efficiently with the neurological unity which he has mastered at that particular moment.

———

The case histories above are given as examples for amplifications of the rationale outlined in this work. The author feels that with case histories we can many times relate the data and the information which we are given in such a way as to clarify the concepts upon which they are based.

12

SUMMARY

In summary, the author believes that reading and language problems can be successfully treated in many more instances than is now the case and that reading problems need not exist at all because they can be successfully prevented. The author has gathered his data from such diverse areas as labor rooms, waiting rooms, operating rooms, classrooms and bedrooms and the very varied data indicates that the neurological development and organization of the human organism is the key to language and reading development and to language and reading difficulties.

It is the author's conviction that unless we deal with these factors first, no remedial measures will be universally effective.

The author feels that reading problems should and can be prevented. He feels that the primary responsibility for prevention rests with parents, and that the secondary responsibility for their prevention rests with teachers. He further feels that with proper preventive measures in effect, this very serious problem can be practically eliminated from the educational scene.

The author realizes that these concepts are new and very different, and that all new and different ideas tend to be criticized. It is the sincere hope of the author that both those who agree and those who disagree with this rationale will spend some time in further experimental investigation of this very important problem. It is the author's sincere wish that the future evaluation and discussion of these concepts be the result of continually increasing experimental data as opposed to the natural negativeness with which new and different ideas are sometimes approached.

A General Bibliography has been included for those who wish to delve into this problem further. A reading of this material will, in terms of background data, bring the reader up to the point at which the author began his studies and up to the point at which this book begins.

The author assures the reader that he plans to continue to gather experimental and clinical data which cast further light on this difficult but fascinating problem.

13

GENERAL BIBLIOGRAPHY

1. Anderson, I. and Hughes, B.: The Relationship Between Learning to Read and Growth as a Whole. *School of Education Bulletin*, (The University of Michigan) Vol. *XXVI*, pp. 65-68, February, 1955.
2. Barger, William C.: An Experimental Approach to Aphasic and to Nonreading Children. *American Journal of Orthopsychiatry*, Vol. *XXIII*, pp. 158-170, January, 1953.
3. Bastian, H. D.: *The Brain as an Organ of the Mind.* London, Kegan, Paul, Trench, Trubner & Co., 1880.
4. Berner, George and Berner, Dorothy: Relation of Ocular Dominance, Handedness and the Controlling Eye in Binocular Vision. *American Medical Association, Archives of Ophthalmology*, Vol. *50*, pp. 603-608, November, 1953.
5. Betts, Emmett A.: A Physiological Approach to the Analysis of Reading Disabilities. *Educational Research Bulletin*, Vol. *XIII*, pp. 135-140; pp. 163-174, September and October, 1934.
6. Blom, E. C.: Mirror Writing. *Psychological Bulletin*, Vol. *XXV*, pp. 582-594, 1928.
7. Boland, John L., Jr.: Type of Birth as Related to Stuttering. *Journal of Speech and Hearing Disorders*, Vol. *XVI*, pp. 40-43, March, 1951.
8. Bryngelson, B.: Laterality of Stutterers and Normal Speakers. *Journal of Social Psychology*, Vol. *II*, pp. 151-155, February, 1940.

9. Bucy, Paul: Organization of Central Nervous System Control of Muscular Activity. *Chicago Medical Society Bulletin,* pp. 836-866, April 30, 1949.

10. Chesher, E. C.: Some Observations Concerning the Relation of Handedness to the Language Mechanism. *Bulletin of the Neurological Institute of New York,* Vol. *IV,* pp. 556-562, 1936.

11. Dearborn, O. W. F.: Ocular and Manual Dominance in Dyslexia. *Psychological Bulletin,* Vol. *28,* p. 704, 1938.

12. Delacato, Carl H.: A Comparison of Two Methods of Teaching Spelling. *Elementary English,* Vol. *XXIX,* No. 1, pp. 26-30, January, 1952.

13. Delacato, Carl H.: Spelling, A Five Year Study. *Elementary English,* Vol. *XXXII,* No. 5, pp. 296-299, May, 1955.

14. Delacato, Carl H.: Hemiplegia and Concomitant Psychological Phenomena. *American Journal of Occupational Therapy,* Vol. *X,* No. 4, Part I, pp. 157 ff., July and August, 1956.

15. Delacato, Janice F. and Delacato, Carl H.: A Group Approach to Remedial Reading, Part I. *Elementary English,* Vol. *XXIX,* pp. 142-149, March, 1952.

16. Delacato, Janice F. and Delacato, Carl H.: A Group Approach to Remedial Reading, Part II, Vol. *XXX,* pp. 31-34, January, 1953.

17. Delacato, Carl H. and Doman, Glenn J.: Propositional Disorders and Their Implications for the Physical Therapist, *The Rehabilitation Forum,* Philadelphia, July, 1956.

18. Delacato, Carl H. and Doman, Glenn J.: Hemiplegia and Concomitant Psychological Phenomena. *American Journal of Occupational Therapy,* Vol. *XI,* No. 4, Part I, pp. 186 ff., July and August, 1957.

19. Delacato, Carl H. and Flores, Anthony: Ideo-Motor Force, An Experimental Rehabilitative Modality. *The Rehabilitation Forum*, Philadelphia, December, 1956.

20. Delacato, Carl H. and Moyer, S. Richard: Can We Teach Word Meaning? *Elementary English*, Vol. *XXX*, No. 3, pp. 102-106, February, 1953.

21. Doman, Glenn J. and Doman, Robert J., and Delacato, Carl H.: The Non-Surgical Central Approach to the Central Problem. *The Rehabilitation Forum*, Philadelphia, January, 1957.

22. Doman, Glenn J., Doman, R., Flores, A., Delacato, C., and Peters, J.: The Non-Surgical Central Approach to the Central Problem, Reflex Therapy. *The Rehabilitation Forum*, Philadelphia, February, 1957.

23. Eames, T. H.: The Anatomical Basis of Lateral Dominance Anomalies. *American Journal of Orthopsychiatry*, Vol. *4*, pp. 524-528, 1934.

24. Eames, T. H.: The Blood Picture in Reading Failure. *Journal of Educational Psychology*, Vol. *XLIV*, pp. 372-375, October, 1953.

25. Eames, T. H.: Comparison of Children of Premature and Full Term Birth Who Fail in Reading. *Journal of Educational Research*, Vol. *XXXVIII*, pp. 506-508, March, 1945.

26. Eastman, Nicholson: Mt. Everest in Utero. *American Journal of Obstetrics and Gynecology*, 67:701, 1954.

27. Eustis, R.: The Primary Etiology of the Specific Language Disabilities. *Journal of Pediatrics*, Vol. *31*, pp. 448-455, October, 1947.

28. Fabian, A.: Reading Disability, An Index of Pathology. *American Journal of Orthopsychiatry*, Vol. *XXIV*, pp. 319-329, April, 1955.

29. Fildes, L. G.: A Psychological Inquiry into the Nature of the Condition Known as Congenital Word Blindness. *Brain*, Vol. *XLIV*, pp. 286-307, 1921-22.

30. Fink, W. H.: The Dominant Eye: Its Clinical Significance. *American Medical Association, Archives of Ophthalmology*, Vol. *19*, pp. 555-582, April, 1938.

31. Freeman, Walter and Watts, James W.: *Psychosurgery*. Springfield, Ill., Charles C Thomas, Publisher, 1942.

32. Gardner, Warren: *Left Handed Writing*. Danville, Ill., Interstate Press, 1945.

33. Goldstein, Kurt: *Aftereffects of Brain Injuries in War*. New York, Grune and Stratton, 1932.

34. Goldstein, Kurt: *Language and Language Disturbances*. New York, Grune and Stratton, 1948.

35. Hallgren, Bertil: Specific Dyslexia (Congenital Word Blindness, A Clinical and Genetic Study), *Acta Psychiatrica Et Meurologica*, Supplement, 65, *XIII*, pp. 287 ff., Norregade, 6, Copenhagen, Denmark: Ejnar Munksgaard, 1950.

36. Head, Henry: Aphasia, An Historical Review. *Brain*, pp. 87-165, 1920.

37. Hildreth, G.: Development and Training of Hand Dominance. *Journal of Genetic Psychology*, Vol. *76*, p. 81, 1950.

38. Hinshelusod, J.: *Congenital Word Blindness*. London, H. K. Lewis and Co. Ltd., 1917.

39. Huber, Mary: Re-education of Aphasics. *Journal of Speech Disorders*, Vol. *VII*, pp. 289-293, December, 1942.

40. Hughes, J., Leander, R., and Ketchum, G.: Electroencephalographic Study of Specific Reading Disabilities. *Electroencephelography and Neurophysiology*, Vol. 1, pp. 377-378, August, 1948.

41. Johnson, P. W.: The Relation of Certain Anomalies of Vision and Lateral Dominance to Reading Disability. *Monographs of the Society for Research in Child Development*, Vol. 7, No. 2, Washington, D.C., National Research Council, 1942.

42. Johnson, Marjorie S.: Factors Relating to Disability in Reading. *Journal of Experimental Education*, Vol. 26, pp. 1-21, September, 1957.

43. Jones, M.: Relationship Between Reading Deficiencies and Left Handedness. *School and Society*, Vol. LX, pp. 238-239, October 7, 1944.

44. Kennedy, Helen: Reversale, Reversale, Reversals! *Journal of Experimental Education*, Vol. XXIII, pp. 161-171, December, 1954.

45. Krise, Morely: An Experimental Investigation of Theories of Reversals in Reading. *Journal of Educational Psychology*, Vol. XLIII, pp. 408-422, November, 1952.

46. Lashley, K. S.: Functional Determinants of Cerebral Localization. *Archives of Neurology and Psychiatry*, Vol. 38, pp. 371-387, August, 1937.

47. Leavell, V.: The Problem of Symbol Reversals and Confusions, Their Frequency and Remediation. *Peabody Journal of Education*, XXXII, pp. 130-141, November, 1954.

48. Lester, R. and Wheeler, V.: Dyslexaphoria, Symptoms and Remedial Suggestions. *Elementary English*, Vol. XXXII, No. 5, pp. 305-311, May, 1955.

49. Martin, Kenneth L.: Handedness: A Review of the Literature on the History, Development and Research of Laterality Preference. *Journal of Educational Research*, Vol. XLV, pp. 527-533, March, 1952.

50. Morgan, W. P.: A Case of Congenital Word Blindness. *British Medical Journal*, Vol. II, p. 1612, November, 1896.

51. Orton, S. T.: An Impediment to Learning to Read, A Neurological Explanation of the Reading Disability. *School and Society, XXVIII,* pp. 286-290, 1928.

52. Orton, S. T.: Certain Failures in the Acquisition of Written Language: Their Bearing on the Problem of Cerebral Dominance. *Archives of Neurology and Psychiatry,* Vol. *XXII,* pp. 841-850, 1929.

53. Park, George E.: Nurture and/or Nature Cause Reading Difficulties? *Archives of Pediatrics,* Vol. *LXIX,* pp. 432-444, November, 1952.

54. Park, George E., et al.: Biological Changes Associated with Dyslexia. *Archives of Pediatrics,* Vol. *LXXII,* pp. 71-84, March, 1955.

55. Penfield, W. and Rasmussen, T.: *The Cerebral Cortex of Man.* New York, The Macmillan Co., 1950.

56. Preston, Ralph C. and Schneyer, J. W.: The Neurological Background of Nine Severely Retarded Readers. *Journal of Educational Research,* Vol. *XLIX,* pp. 455-459, February, 1956.

57. Rapaport, David: *Organization and Pathology of Thought.* New York, Columbia University Press, 1951, p. 786.

58. Sall, M. and Wepman, J. M.: A Screening Survey of Organic Impairment. *Journal of Speech Disorders,* Vol. *X,* pp. 283-286, May, 1945.

59. Selzer, C. A.: Lateral Dominance and Visual Fusion: Their Application in Reading, Writing, Spelling, and Speech. *Harvard Monographs in Education.* Cambridge, Mass., Harvard University Press, 1933, No. 12.

60. Shilder, Paul: Congenital Alexia and its Relation to Optic Perception. *The Journal of Genetic Psychology, LXV,* No. 1, pp. 67-88, September, 1944.

61. Smith, Linda: A Study of Laterality Characteristics of Retarded Readers and Reading Achievers. *Journal of Experimental Education*, Vol. *XVIII*, pp. 321-329, June, 1950.

62. Steinberg, P. and Rosenberg, R.: Relationship Between Reading and Various Aspects of Visual Anomalies. *Journal of the American Optometric Association*, Vol. *XXVI*, pp. 444-446, March, 1956.

63. Stevenson, L. and Robinson, H.: Eye-Hand Preference, Reversals and Reading Progress, Clinical Studies in Reading. II. Supplementary Educational Monographs No. 77, pp. 83-88, University of Chicago Press, 1953.

64. Tyler, Fred T.: Organismic Growth: Sexual Maturity and Progress in Reading. *Journal of Educational Psychology*, Vol. *XLVI*, pp. 85-93, February, 1955.

65. Van Riper, Charles: The Quantitative Measure of Laterality. *Journal of Experimental Psychology*, Vol. *XVIII*, pp. 372-382, June, 1935.

66. Walls, G. L.: Theory of Ocular Dominance, American Medical Association. *Archives of Ophthalmology*, Vol. *45*, pp. 387-415, April, 1951.

67. Weber, C. O.: Strephosymbolia and Reading Disability. *Journal of Abnormal and Social Psychology*, *XXXIX*, pp. 356-361, July, 1944.

68. Wechsler, Israel: *Textbook of Clinical Neurology*. W. B. Saunders Co., Philadelphia, 1939.

69. Weisenburg, T. H.: A Study of Aphasia. *Archives of Neurology and Psychiatry*, *XXXI*, pp. 1-33, 1934.

70. Zollinger, R.: Removal of Left Cerebral Hemisphere. *Archives of Neurology and Psychiatry*, Vol. *34*, pp. 1055-1064, November, 1935.

INDEX

A

Allergies, 7
Ambidexterity, 23, 54, 101
Amblyopia, 62
Amphibious level, 27, 30
Anaesthesia, 73
Anatomy, neural, 34
Ancient reflexes, 16
Anoxia, 45, 73, 103
Anti-tropic patterns, 11
Aphasia, 15, 23, 47
Aqueduct of Sylvius, 27
Archery, 69
Area Striata, 27
Arithmetic, 6, 9, 85
Arm, immobilization of, 56, 89
Associative level, 9, 10, 94
Asthma, 7
Ataxia, 51
Athletics, 92, 96
Attentionality, 49
Attitude, 7
Awareness, external, 10

B

Babinsky reflex, 53
Baseball, 84
Basketball, 84, 90
Beecham, C. T., 46
Berner, George and Dorothy, 57
Bilateral lesion, 10
Birth, 8, 13, 23, 73, 95, 101
Blindness, 87
Blood pressure, 26
Body temperature, 26
Boys as reading problems, 5
Braille, 88
Brain, 13, 45, 47, 82
Breathing, 26

C

California Test of Mental Maturity, 68
Carbon dioxide, 49
Carrington, E., 46
Cerebral palsy, 44
Cerebral vascular accident, 93
Cerebro-spinal system, 27, 50, 57
Choking, 7
College admissions, 89
Communication, 15
Comparative anatomy, 26
Comprehension scores, 8
Confusion, hand-eye, 61
Conservative schools, 6
Coordination, 7
Cortex, 10, 15, 19, 22, 24, 46
Crayoning, 76
Crib placement, 75
Crying, 73
Cutaneous innervation, 34

D

da Vinci, 54
Dexterity, 16, 95
Divorce, 6
Dominance, 13, 15, 57, 60
Dressing children, 75

E

Eating utensils, 76
Educational bias, 3
Electroencephalogram, 49, 53, 106
Emotions, 4, 6
Engram, 11
Evolution, 18, 21
Exhibitionism, 6

119

120

Trumpet playing, 90